#1 Equine IgG
On Site Quantitative
Testing

VDx

974 Silver Bend Road
Belgium, WI 53004

Toll Free: 866-451-2499
Ph: 262-675-2499
Fax: 262-675-0629

VETERINARY DIAGNOSTICS

www.vetdx.biz

The Dream Race
The Search for the Greatest
Thoroughbred Race Horse of All Time
written and illustrated by

Robert Clark

Published by: Horse & Dragon Publishing
Post Office Box 372388
Satellite Beach, FL 32937
orders@horsedragon.com
Rights reserved

Copyright 2004
ISBN 0-9759488-0-6
Library of Congress Control Number: 2004111064
Includes 12 Color plates

Printed in United States
First Edition: Nov. 2004

HORSE & DRAGON
PUBLISHING

Dedicated to

Nichole, Courtney, & Rylee

A special thank you to all the people who have been there when the writer needed them:
My mother, Jim Wooldridge, Nikki Smart-Davis, Jean Yves & Denise Clerc, Monte & Colleen Tobin,
Bob Simpson, Johnie Welch, Ann Peters, Inge Manders, Dr. Ed Carlos, Lori Spry, Bill Brill, Kurt Koening,
Dr. Ron Bibb, Dr. Jerry & Debra Pack, Ed Bowen, Marci Smith, Richard Stone Reeves, Karen Hickok,
John & Teresa Thorley, Dr. Bill & Joyce Corwin, Cheryl Davis, Charlie & Gloria Velek, and Bobby Rahal.

A very special thank you goes to
Brian Clark, my photographer, computer expert, and most of all, my brother;
without his tireless efforts the <u>Dream Race</u> would be just a dream and not a reality.

Preface

Preface

The <u>Dream Race</u>, the book and series of paintings, I created was a fanciful way of addressing the question of who is the greatest thoroughbred champion of all-time; but, maybe for you, the reader, another question is, why a <u>Dream Race</u>? My candid answer may surprise some people, but it tells of the challenge of being an artist and being financially successful while doing what you want to do.

The first big lesson I learned traveling the country with my artwork was that the quality of the artwork from an artistic standpoint and the ability to sell it were largely unrelated. A great piece of art on the canvas doesn't necessarily translate into income in the pocket. In 1982, I went to the Arabian Nationals in Kentucky with several pieces of art taken straight from the Arabian magazines. Each piece of 30 pastels in my inventory was instantly recognized as the specific horse I painted. What I learned was that people didn't want to buy a painting of someone else's horse, they wanted their horse immortalized. The obvious answer was to do commissions and over the years I have painted countless horses and riders on a commission basis.

The other piece of advice I heeded after the Arabian Nationals was to begin painting thoroughbreds. Twenty years ago, a horse was horse. I see thoroughbreds now as athletes in a sport with long, rich history. The more I painted thoroughbreds, the more I became a sponge of horse racing history. This was never an intended direction for my career or my artwork, it just happened as I read everything I could get my hands on regarding thoroughbred and horse racing.

As an artist, there was something missing for me personally doing portrait work. Some of my best paintings have been portraits, but I have always been more interested in action scenes, sporting events, complex images, and historical significance. Since my days as a college artist, my paintings have always wanted to tell a story. One professor described my paintings as being 'very lyrical'; in retrospect it was a rather prophetic critique.

Over a seven year span I wrote my first novel, <u>The Elements of Perspective</u>; a historical fiction based in the dilemma of art versus censorship. I called upon my background in art history and my knowledge of horses to add depth to the story and a key role in the plot. However, I never mixed my paintings with my writing to enhance the story. The <u>Dream Race</u> changed that. By the time I finished the second painting, I saw the value words could provide as a means of filling in the details for you; the viewer / reader. The <u>Dream Race</u> gave me the opportunity to present your eye with several short stories on canvas, while whispering the lyrics into your ear. I hope you enjoy this visual fantasy and its unique version of a thoroughbred racing history lesson.

Robert Clark, author & artist

The Meeting

This is a story about an extraordinary individual named Leonard Tharpe and the "Dream Race". Before I get ahead of myself, my name is Allen Clemens. I'm a writer; how good a writer is a matter of opinion. I always wanted to write the "great American novel", but I never seemed to find the time to work on it around my schedule writing for the local newspaper. I've been working for this small town paper since I graduated college. I was an honor student and have a stack of poems, short stories, and essays to my credit that I feel are of excellent quality; but I seem to be a minority of one. I grew up playing sports, so when this little newspaper in a small town called Paris needed a sports writer; I suddenly remembered making the Little League all-star team and watching all of our high school football games from the bench. Hey, they wanted a sports-writer, not Michael Jordan, right? Besides, writing is in my blood. Clemens, yeah that's right, I'm related to him, you know, the guy better known as Mark Twain. I'm some distant cousin or nephew through my father's father's father, but other than that; I have no clue what the relation is. It was just one of those things that came up at family reunions. It was either that or talk about Aunt Evelyn's diabetes or Uncle Elmer's bad ticker. After all these years, it's still ticking and we all attribute it to his radiator staying topped-off with his home-made corn antifreeze, you know – moonshine, the elixir of life South of the Mason Dixon line. If Ponce de Leon had ever met my uncle, the explorer might have found the elusive Fountain of Youth at the bottom of one of Uncle Elmer's jugs.

But, I digress. Writing is in my blood, even if it means writing for a newspaper that prides itself on being able to combine the social pages with the obituaries. It's really not too different from writing for the New Yorker or one of those high society magazines, because if you aren't on the social page you might as well be dead. Our local paper also lists the police reports; you know, the 'who was arrested for public drunkenness or who ran over their neighbor's mailbox, of course the answer is usually one and the same, whoever it was that most recently paid Uncle Elmer a visit. That's big news around here and seriously it's one of the great things about this town and maybe any small town. News usually comes in small bites that are easily digestible with a cup of coffee and biscuit with sorghum molasses. It's not my thing, but in a small town, you need to make an effort to fit in. "Fittin' in" seems to be the most important thing in these parts and when you come from the outside, you do what you're asked; especially when it's your brand new boss doing the asking.

I was on the job with the paper for not even a week when the editor asked me what I knew about horse racing. Well, did I mention that when I was riding the pine at the ball game, I was also riding my stallion back at the family farm? OK, so it wasn't a stallion . . . it wasn't even a horse. It was a gelded Shetland pony, but it had a real bad attitude. Well, he was at least as difficult to ride as the mechanical horse in front of Wal-Mart. That pony required incredible equestrian skills to stay in the saddle, which meant my brother and I must have been real cowboys, because we didn't even own a saddle. Yeah, so suddenly I'm the expert for the newspaper smack dab in the middle of horse racing country.

"Hey, Kid," that's what Mr. Williams always called me. I swear he didn't know my name and that way, if I stuck around long enough then he would eventually learn it and no one would be any the wiser. I am sure it was a pragmatic approach to business management. After all, why learn the name of every kid with a pencil and notepad who says he's a journalist? Lucky for me, I'm still here; but he still calls me "Kid". I assume he knows my name; then, again maybe not, because I do remember him calling me "Twain". Oh well, did I mention it was nice to have family contacts . . . however remote or impossible to substantiate they may be?

"Hey, Kid, I want you to do a story about horse racing and I've got an idea."

Less than a month out of college and when he said, "jump"; I asked, "how high?"

"Yes, sir, Mr. Williams," I had good upbringing and that was a good thing, because as much as I wasn't sure if he knew my name; I was convinced his first name was "Sir".

"I want you to write a story about the greatest thoroughbred of all time."

The Dream Race

"Yes, sir," I waited for him to fill in the obvious blank, the name of the horse, the one who was the greatest thoroughbred of all-time. The pause became silence and I began to panic as apparently he thought I knew the answer to such a simple question. It was so simple; he didn't even have to tell me who it was. After waiting a minute in sheer terror I was about to ask the potentially embarrassing question, when the thought occurred to me that if it was such an obvious answer, even if I didn't know who the-greatest-thoroughbred-of-all-time was, someone would know. I mean how many people would I have to ask? One, maybe two at the most, right?

Wrong!!! The first person I asked said one name; but I was too good an investigative journalist to leave it at one source. So, I asked someone else. You guessed it, I got a different answer. The more I asked the more names came into the mix. Several horses were mentioned over and over, but the fact was that there was no one clear cut "greatest thoroughbred of all-time". The problem was simple. I had to be asking the wrong people. These people weren't experts. I needed to speak to the experts and the experts would love to speak with me, remember – I write for the newspaper and that's almost as good as being on television.

The best place to find an expert was where they hang out. In horse racing that would have to be the race track, right? I took my notepad, laptop, palm pilot, tape recorder, cell phone, camera, and . . . oh yeah, my pencil; then headed to the nearest track. At the track I used a new strategy. Instead, of asking the question of who was the greatest horse of all-time, my objective was to identify the experts and then ask them. As I asked around I was steered towards a couple of trainers, a couple of jockeys, and a few breeders. There was still no consensus to my editor's question. Maybe, I should just go back to him and admit I didn't know who the greatest horse of all-time was. Never! The great thing about being young is never having to say, "I don't know", much less, "I was wrong".

About this time I was directed to one of the most interesting people I have ever met. The 'trackies' all said I should speak with Leonard. His name was not only brought up as an expert by the experts, but it was brought up with a kind of hollowed reverence. Leonard, a life long stable hand, was a tiny, shriveled man who was well into his eighties, maybe even nineties. His mouth was constantly filled with a chew of tobacco. In his own words, "You can't burn a barn down with a chew, plus it keeps the hands free." The chaw in his mouth didn't leave any room for a bad word towards any one; even if an occasional curse rolled over his lips – it was more for artistic color than vulgarity. His eyes were lucid and clear, but when he started to talk about horses they lit up from the inside like a lighthouse, a beacon in the dark. That was it, he was an oracle in the world of horse racing; a world filled with fanatic fervor. He was both a historian and guru. Leonard had filed away so much information; he was a walking encyclopedia of horse racing. His mind worked like a computer as he accessed his incredible data base of memories. Leonard's storytelling brought these bits of history to life. The result was like watching a full color movie suitable for nomination for an Academy Award. Oh yeah, I could see a whole slew of Oscars sprawled over his bedroom dresser. Did I say Slew?

When I found Leonard he had a smile across his face as if he was meeting an old friend. I even tried to remember, if maybe we had met somewhere before. Just when I let the thought pass, he said to me, "I've been expecting you."

"What?" I answered.

"I wondered when you would find me," Leonard said. He smiled. His teeth looked as if they had chewed their way through a couple miles of tobacco, but that didn't deter his smile in the least bit.

"You're Leonard, Leonard Tharpe?"

"That's right." He looked at me as if he knew what my words were going to be. It was like talking to Yoda in Star Wars. He was this miniscule, diminutive figure who would go unnoticed by the millions of people passing through the gates at the track; yet the people behind the scenes recognized him and even looked up to him, which was ironic considering in his current shriveled state he was shorter than most jockeys.

What was it that made this man special? I couldn't answer that at first, but knowing him a little better now, I can

The Dream Race

honestly say it is love; the love of horses, racing, and the world we outsiders call the track. To us, the track is a place or a thing. To people like Leonard it is a paradise. Of course, Leonard smiles often and laughs easily; wouldn't you, if you were living on Cloud 9 surrounded by four-legged angels? If you asked Leonard if he believed in heaven, he would only look around and say, "That's where the Dream Race is."

"Dream race? What's the dream race, Leonard?" He could tell I was hooked; giving him an audience for his favorite story, a story he had polished over the years.

"That's why you wanted to talk to me, right? You wanted to hear about the Dream Race. You want to know about the greatest thoroughbred of all-time, don't you?"

"Yeah, how did you know that? Oh, I guess people told you, I'd been asking around."

Leonard smiled again and shook his head.

"No?"

"You're a reporter, right?"

"Yes, and more than one person has told me, if I wanted to know the greatest horse of all-time, I should talk to you."

"You work for Mr. Williams. Am I right?"

"Yes," Suddenly, I think I knew how a fish on a hook might feel.

"Boy, you ain't the first."

"What?"

"Mr. Williams has a favorite test he puts his new reporters through. He asks them to write a story about the greatest thoroughbred of all-time. By my count you may be the fourth or fifth one given this assignment."

"You talked to them . . . these other writers?"

"Nah, none of them ever talked to me. I saw 'em and then saw their columns."

"And . . . ?"

"Well, you can relax 'cause they all got the answer wrong. You see, only the horses can answer that question and they have to do it the only way they know how, at full speed."

"What do you mean?" I wasn't too sure about this strange, little man.

"None of those other writers ever heard about the Dream Race."

"Why not?" I asked.

"Look at me. I'm just an old stable hand, not a famous trainer or Hall-of-Fame jockey; what could I possibly know? Let's be honest, if I was a book, this old black man would never get taken off the shelf. Not supposed to judge a book by its cover, but everyone does and I guess the worst ones are young writers on the fast lane to some place they call Success. They're in too much of a hurry to learn what they're writing about. Mr. Williams is no fool, far from it. He can tell by the way a kid handles this one question, if he's a reporter or just a flash-in-the-pan. So, what are you?"

"Excuse me?"

"Are you a writer or a flash-in-the-pan?"

"A writer!" I asserted with bravado, before I even had time to answer the question to myself. The truth was, before I met Leonard, I didn't even know the answer to that question.

"Well, then . . . are you interested in hearing about the Dream Race?"

"Yes . . ." Keep in mind at this point I still wasn't sure, if I was talking with a raving lunatic whose mind had turned to mush mucking stalls all of his life or if this truly was the enlightened spirit my guts (my writer's guts I later learned) were telling me he was. I looked at my watch.

"Don't do that again."

"What?" I asked.

"Look at your watch. If you've got somewhere else to go, then go; but if I'm gonna tell you about the Dream Race, I would appreciate it if you don't do that again while I'm talkin'. Deal?"

The Dream Race

"Fair enough." I answered. Leonard had a presence that can't be given with a job title. You can't buy it and it can't be taken from you; you either have it or you don't. Leonard definitely had it.

"Mr. Williams asked you a simple question when he gave you this assignment; he also gave you one that can't be answered."

"Yeah, a lot of people have told me that too." I realized a good writer has to respect someone else's right to tell their story. "I'm sorry, Mr. Tharpe, I won't interrupt you again." He smiled. Why did I suddenly call him Mr. Tharpe? I still don't know other than it was the same respect I would have shown to any of my schoolteachers or preachers from my childhood. I had a feeling Mr. Tharpe was about to continue my education in more ways than one.

"Fair enough." Leonard answered using my own words. You guessed it, he smiled and this time so did I.

"Where do we begin?" I asked.

"First we have to establish some ground rules to the Dream Race."

I nodded my quiet agreement.

"To begin, this is like when those computers play a baseball game with the New York Yankees from the '20s with Babe Ruth and Lou Gehrig versus the Big Red Machine with Pete Rose, Johnny Bench, and Joe Morgan fifty years later. The outcome is only as good as the computer and the person putting the info in that little box. In the Dream Race there is no computer, just me and the better part of a century living and breathing horses. I've seen the Dream Race in my head a thousand times. The second thing to keep in mind, this is that the Dream Race is a whole day of races, imaginary races. So, there's a lot of things different from other races," Leonard's eyes seemed to focus on his memories the way the rest of us look at what right under our noses.

"What kind of differences?" My question didn't seem to be as much an interruption as it was an opportunity for Leonard to build his stage.

"These Dream Races are in heaven. Do you know what heaven is?" I shrugged my shoulders. I was beginning to get the feeling Leonard wasn't all there, but something made you believe he knew what he was talking about. "I'll tell you what heaven is. Heaven is Hialeah in the winter, Churchill Downs and Pimlico in May, Belmont Park in June, Saratoga in the summer, and Santa Anita in the fall. Heaven is all the great places where the great horses ran. It's the day when every eye focuses on one place like a giant magnifying glass; when the crowds push in shoulder to shoulder hoping to get a peek at greatness; that's heaven!" Leonard caught his breath and I held mine.

"Only in heaven can the horses still be seen running at Hialeah. The track is closed now, but Hialeah was the start of the racing season and almost every horse in the field of the Dream Race began their careers racing at Hialeah. For nearly seventy years this is where the world got an early look at who the best horses would be for that year. Since Hialeah's opening just about every Triple Crown winner spent their winter running at Hialeah. Boy, you can't imagine how beautiful a track Hialeah was unless you'd been there. It was like a tropical paradise, all those flowers, palm trees, and the pink flamingos in the lake in the infield. This sport has a lot of great sites, but one of my favorites was when they'd blow a horn and those pink flamingos would fly a big circle around the track and then land right back where they took off from. It was hard not to stop what you were doing just to stand there and watch 'em. It was better than any halftime show. The back-side of Hialeah was like the Garden of Eden and a shrine to horse racing all in one. There was a life size sculpture of Citation and every where you looked were plaques describing something out of the pages of history, something that happened right there where you'd be standing.

"The great tracks like Churchill Downs, Pimlico, and Belmont, where the three legs of the Triple Crown are run and maybe even out to California, to Del Mar and Santa Anita where the horse race under the back drop of the purple mountains on the horizon while being squeezed between all those Hollywood movie types."

The Dream Race

Without a word Leonard pulled out his wallet. He reached into the space were most people keep folding money. He pulled out a well-worn sheet of blue lined notebook paper falling apart at the edges that had been neatly sheared off at the folds. He handed it to me.

"What's this?" I asked.

"You tell me."

I glanced at it as I held the paper delicately as it drooped over my hands. For every name I recognized there were dozens I didn't.

"These are some of the horses who will go to the post at a little track called Heaven. I can tell you are in a hurry to be some place. If that place isn't a place called Success, you'll come back when you have more time."

"When do you what me to come back?"

"Meet me at Memaw's, it's a little restaurant you have to pass on the way here. I'll buy you breakfast."

"Mr. Tharpe, what time would breakfast happen to be?"

"I'll be there at five." He said without blinking. Man, I wish he would've at least blinked.

"In the morning …. Tomorrow morning?" I was horrified. What had I gotten myself into? I folded up the faded piece of paper and handed it back to him. "I'll see you then." I must have really been desperate for this job, nothing else could explain the words coming out of my mouth.

"Keep it, son. I know who's on the list. By the way, you may want to call Mr. Williams and ask for the day off tomorrow. Tell him you're helping me; I've got a lot of work to do and I could use a hand."

I thanked Leonard for his time and assured him I'd be there for breakfast. I was still too numb at the thought of meeting him at 5:00 a.m. to realize I had just committed myself to a day of work. Surely, he wasn't really going to make me work, was he? I vowed to learn as much as I could about the names on this withered piece of paper before I came back. But, how much could I learn in one night, one short night, because somebody was going to bed early tonight.

The concept of the Dream Race was more than I had expected to find, but my instinct told me it was exactly the story I was looking for. You know, those writer's instincts that develop over a life-time of journalism, or in my case they just came packed inside my guts that were doing somersaults with excitement. Mr. Williams look out – here comes the Dream Race...

The Dream Race

Ladies First: The Dream Distaff features several 'ladies' from the later twentieth century racing under the watchful eye of Regret the first female winner of the Kentucky Derby in 1915.

Ladies First

Did you know it's pitch black at 5:00 in the morning? Well, I didn't and as far as I was concerned, I hoped I would never know it again. I'm driving down some narrow country road with one eye half open and the other still on my pillow. Driving by memory would work, if I had actually been to the place where I was going. I thought, 'they'd better have coffee waiting for me when I get there; wherever there was.' Just as my half opened eye was about to rejoin the other one in

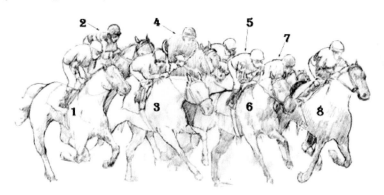

Ladies First

1. Genuine Risk
2. Serena's Song
3. Lady's Secret
4. Personal Ensign
5. Winning Colors
6. Azeri
7. Go For Wand
8. Ruffian

Sleepyland, the site of a shack with all the lights on caught my attention. This had to be it. The next question was who belonged to all these cars. I mean the parking lot was full. You mean to tell me other people were up at this time? Was I crazy? If I was, it looks like I had plenty of company.

The sign was lit with a simple flood light: Memaw's. I rolled out of my car with the same motion I used to leave the comfy confines of my bed. Sleep walking was the only explanation I could come up with for getting from there to here. I didn't need coffee as much as I thought I would, when my first step hit a puddle. It was an omen, an ominous omen warning me of the pre-dawn demon better known as 'Daybreak'. He was out there and this puddle had to be the first of his dirty tricks. My childhood fear of the dark didn't seem so silly any more. My innate survival instincts screamed to get inside. I burst through the doors to a room full of staring eyes. What? OK, so I was a stranger to this regular gathering of early birds. They looked at me as if I was Daybreak coming to get them.

It was then that I heard a laugh coming from the back of the diner. By the time I saw Leonard waving to me from a booth in the back, the rest of the room was smiling and chuckling. One cherub-faced waitress said, "Honey, your horses are getting out." I stared at her. She must've had me confused with someone else, I don't have any horses. "Your barn door's open and your horses are getting out." She repeated while pointing.

So, I did what any pre-dawn demon would do; I checked my zipper. As I feared, I'd rushed out of the house a little prematurely; another evil trick perpetrated by 'Daybreak'. With my pride wounded and the demon put to rest, I slunk towards Leonard's booth.

"I hope those are the last horses you let get loose today." Leonard was enjoying my moment of embarrassment along with everyone else. "Well, son, now that you had time to look at the list, any comments?" Leonard said as he started to rebuild the chaw in his mouth fresh from his Beechnut pouch. It was his flavor of choice for over sixty years. I was still more of an Eggs Benedict man myself and of course served with a silver spoon. This was going to be long day. As far as I was concerned, it already was. I slid into the booth and waved to the cherub for coffee, the cure for pre-dawn demons.

I wasn't sure how to reply without offending him. After all, everyone on the backside said he was the one to ask. Yet, his ancient list had so many names of horses I'd never heard of. I did a little homework the night before we met. I knew there had been eleven Triple Crown winners. His list had more than eleven, so I figured it was those eleven plus a couple more. When I checked closer, there were several Triple Winners that weren't on Leonard's list. My dilemma was how to tell Leonard his list wasn't going to be much help, if it was prone to such obvious omissions while having some rather obscure horses in their place.

"Leonard, I appreciate your time; but I don't think this . . . you see . . . I was supposed to be . . ."

I stammered as I tried to be polite, but Leonard just stared at me. The more I stammered the more my polite approach seemed less than sincere. Then, I noticed the smile on the old man's face. It grew until his brown teeth snuck out between his cracked lips.

"Good morning, to you too" Leonard said as I took my first sip. "Don't worry, son, it's early. You'll understand soon enough."

"I'm sorry, good morning, Leonard."

The eggs and bacon were finished and all that was left was the early morning conversation, consisting of the next verbal pages of the Dream Race. Leonard leaned into the smoke wafting from the adjacent table as if a reformed smoker remembering some lost pleasure. He looked back at me and smiled.

"Boy, the Dream Race ain't just one race. It's a whole day of races, just like any other day at the track, but it ain't just any other day; that's for sure."

Leonard forgot about the smoke as his mind drifted into its own haze. It wasn't a haze resulting from the lack of clarity. It was the exact opposite. His concentration was zeroed in on his story. He was taking a moment to review the images in his mind before he narrated another chapter in the Dream Race.

"That's right, a whole card of races. Kinda like a boxing match. There may be the big headline fight the crowd has come to see, but there are a series of fights to whet the appetite. Same thing except instead of standing toe-to-toe, these champions rub against each other at break neck speeds." Leonard said with a laugh.

"What's so funny?"

"Boy, have ya ever seen a cat fight?"

"A cat fight?" My rephrasing of his question added to his amusement as he burst into all out laughter.

"Yeah, they can make even Mohammed Ali shake in his boots when they get all riled up."

"Leonard, are we talking about horse racing or boxing?"

"Sometimes there ain't much difference when you look at the conditioning, the strategy, and the heart of the athlete. No one dared questioned Ali's heart."

"But, he was afraid of cats?" My question gave Leonard further reason to laugh.

The Dream Race

"Not a cat with four legs and a tail; boy, I'm talking 'bout the two legged kind. Their claws are sharper, that's for sure."

"Ali was afraid of women?"

"Boy, would you forget 'bout Ali for second. We're talkin' 'bout a cat fight."

"When you say cats you mean women, right?'

"Females, son, that's what I'm talkin' about. If you want to see heart on a athlete you look at a woman. People think men are athletes, nah sir. If an athlete is measured by their heart, then the female of any species has a head start on their physically stronger counterparts. When a woman wants to win, don't get in her way; it might not be too safe. There's only one reason why there wasn't any women gladiators; the Romans had second thoughts 'bout handing a woman a weapon. Yes sir, women may not like to fight, they may not show their competitive side like men do; but make no mistake, when a woman goes to war she's not there to take prisoners. It's hard to say if it's pride, motherly instincts, or a secret competitive nature; but women play to win and they offer no apologies for it when they do."

"So, this race is with females only."

"Uh huh, but mind you, the Dream Race is what every body wants to see. Everybody wants to know who is the greatest of all time; but truth be known, the best race of the day would probably be the Dream Distaff."

"Dream Distaff?"

"Boy, you ain't exactly up on your track lingo, are you? Distaff is a race for the females; the fillies and mares."

"The girls don't run with the boys?"

"Occasionally they do. It's rare when one of the girls wins, but it's instantly history when it happens in one of the big races. Those races make history, while making legends out of the winners. Yeah, that's the stuff dreams are made of."

Mastering the art of interviewing, which I now had a sum total of about thirty minutes experience; I was able to ask Leonard several of my scintillating questions with nothing more than the dumb look on my face.

"So, you want an example of history. History is Regret." Leonard said.

Even the dumb look on my face couldn't keep my mouth from jumping in. "History is regret. Oh, I see you're being philosophical. Don't you think that's a little bleak?"

"Well, it might mean one thing to Julius Caesar or Napoleon; but in horse racing Regret is not a bad feelin'. Oh no, on the contrary, it's a great feeling. You see Regret is a horse, a very special horse. She was the first filly to win the Kentucky Derby. It was 1915 and the Derby had been run for nearly fifty years before a filly came along and

Regret

beat the boys in the run for the roses. It would be another sixty-five years before another filly would come along and do it again. For over a hundred years only one horse won the race some called the most famous horse race of 'em all. It was

Regret, a big liver chestnut filly with a blaze that ran the length of her long beautiful face."

"Who else is in the Dream Distaff with Regret?" My question made Leonard grin like a possum.

"Regret is history, but she is not in the Dream Distaff."

"She's not? Why not?"

Leonard set back in his chair. "Well, she's there. She's watching. You see, here's how I see it; the officials believe the other fillies would let Regret win. She's the first queen of racing. Regret watches the Dream Distaff's fabulous fillies like a proud mother. She might not have been the fastest filly of all-time, but none of the other fillies would disrespect her like that. They just wouldn't; 'cause once on the throne, the queen rules forever, and make no mistake, Regret is the queen."

"If she doesn't run, then who is in the race?"

"Let's start with maybe the most famous filly ever. You ever heard of Ruffian?"

"I think I've heard the name."

The Dream Race

"Boy, if there is one horse you had better know, it's that big black-bay filly. She's one of the greatest of all-time and I don't just mean fillies. She never lost a race. In ten races, she led every race at every furlong pole. She went from the starter's gate to the finish line, wire to wire, every time and set track record after track record in the process. Her greatness on the track has been overshadowed."

"By what? What could overshadow such an incredible record?"

"Son, you ever heard the song about the day the music died? It was a plane crash and it took the lives of the young rock-n-roll stars, Buddy Holly, Richie Valens, and the Big Bopper."

"Yeah, the Madonna song," I was proud to finally get an answer correct.

"Don McLean wrote it before you were born. Ask Madonna, I'm sure she'd tell you the same. Well, horse racing has its own version of the day the music died. It was a match race with Ruffian and Foolish Pleasure who had won the Kentucky Derby that year. It was just a couple years after Secretariat electrified the world and brought millions of new fans to the track. The match race between Ruffian and Foolish Pleasure was run at Belmont Park and the world watched live on television. The big filly was probably the most loved horse the track had ever seen. She pulled in front of the colt on the turn when she broke down. Every effort was made to save her, but she had to be put down. Boy, there wasn't a dry eye on earth. If you saw the race, you cried. Many of the new fans Secretariat brought to racing the year before, left with a broken heart."

It had been thirty years and still the whites of Leonard's eyes turned red, until their only relief was to spill a tear down his crinkled cheek. I understand the spell horses have over people. It's not a fist full of dollars and the hope of a winning ticket; it's love; the love of beauty, of heart, the love of family. I ignored the tears on his cheeks out of respect. The old sage made an effort to discreetly sponge them with a paper napkin. Old trainers don't cry about horses, except maybe horses like Ruffian.

After I waited silently for a moment I encouraged Leonard to continue telling about the Dream Distaff. "Who else is in this field?"

"You mean who is running for second in the Dream Distaff?" Even in Leonard's imagination, he couldn't see the outcome any other way. "Well, the next one would be the first filly to win the Derby after Regret. 1980 was the year Genuine Risk wore the roses at Churchill Downs. She was a big chestnut filly with a wide blaze down her face. Along with her is another Derby winner, the gray filly, Winning Colors. She ran for Eugene Klein's farm. He also owned the San Diego Chargers in the National Football League. His silks had the blue and gold of his football team emblazed with their trademark lightning bolt. Mr. Klein had another fantastic filly named Lady Secret. By the time she was finished racing she was almost snow white. She was a daughter of the great Secretariat. Many will tell you she was his best, male or female."

"Winning Colors is linked with another filly in what some call one of the greatest races of all-time. Personal Ensign was a beautiful bay filly run by Ogden Phipps in their black silks and red cap. Her red coat trimmed by her black mane and tail mirroring the Phipps' silks was one of the most stunning sights at the track. I think they looked so good when the jockey was put on her that she won most of her races before they even left the paddock area. The final meeting between Winning Colors and Personal Ensign was a classic duel as Personal Ensign edged out a victory in the Breeders' Cup Distaff to retire undefeated."

"Who else is in the Dream Distaff?"

"Serena's Song was another filly who not only ran with the boys, she beat 'em. Her win in the '95 Haskell is still talked about as one of the most exciting races as she pulled the victory away from a field of colts."

"What else can you tell me about her?"

"She won seventeen stakes races. Winning the Jim Beam stakes helped seal her to the honor of being the three-year-old top filly. What do you expect when you're the only girl and you're beating the boys. It was her turn to strike a blow for women's lib. It's funny how when a filly does come along that can go heads up with the boys, how much the fans adore her. Oh yeah, Serena had a following inside the racing world. Not many horses transcended the sport the way Ruffian did, but Serena's Song was definitely everybody's darling in her day. She was a pretty athlete and loved competition. She lost by a head as a two year old in the Breeders' Cup to the undefeated Flanders. It was the tough stretch drive that let everyone know she had the heart. After that loss, if she got a horse one-on-one in the homestretch, she was pretty automatic; she was gonna put 'em away; just like she did in the Hollywood Starlet when she nosed Urbane at the wire. Yeah, she was the 'Hollywood Starlet', all right."

"Hollywood Starlet? That's a little melodramatic don't you think?" I asked.

"Not really, she was a California girl, out there with all those movie stars. She was trained by D. Wayne Lukas. He kinda looks like a Hollywood Cowboy with his big smile and even bigger cowboy hat. Nobody said it better than Mr. Lukas when he said Serena's Song had the elegance of Grace Kelly, the moves of Ginger Rogers, and the charm of Marilyn Monroe. Now, that's a compliment . . . that is if you're not too young to get it."

"I get it. She could really dance around the track."

"And she looked mighty fine doing it, just like a Hollywood starlet should." Leonard said and then sat up in his seat. Normally, I was nearly a foot taller than him, but now he seemed to grow as if getting back all the inches time and hard work had taken from him. He looked me square in the eye.

"Along with Ruffian, there is another tragic member of this elite group of ladies. Her name is Go For Wand. She broke down and had to be put down in the Breeders' Cup Distaff. Before that, she had only one loss in two years. When she was right, she was virtually unbeatable. She showed great heart as she never gave anything less than her best. Horses can block pain and fear with the sheer strength of their heart pounding in their chest, pumping every drop of blood in their veins. They'll give you everything and that's exactly the kind of filly Go For Wand was."

Leonard rubbed his nose as if scratching it, but I'm sure he was holding back tears. He glanced around the room making sure no one saw him. There's a toughness expected by people at the track. Leonard had it, but he also had what so

many of the toughest guys had, a soft spot filled with passion for these creatures. Leonard hid it; even if the whites of his eyes were red again. In due time, when Leonard was ready, he continued.

"There is one last horse who has recently joined the girls for ladies' night."

"Who's that?"

"Her name is Azeri. She wears the red, white, and blue silks made famous by one of the greats of all-time, Cigar. The blue sleeves speckled with white stars and the chest and back have the red and blue A P of the late Allen Paulson. Mr. Paulson's son, Michael, runs the racing program now. You have to be proud of how the young man has stepped out of his father's shadow to put together one of the longest winning streaks the track has seen in years. She may not be an immortal yet, but she's laid the ground work for a Hall-of-Fame career. Azeri was one of a very select few fillies to be named Horse-of-the-Year. It's one thing to beat the boys in a race; it's something else to take the top honor for the whole year. Calumet's Twilight Tear was the first filly to do it in

1943. I guarantee you, Mike Smith, Azeri's Hall-of-Fame jockey got the itch when he ran out of fingers to keep track of her winning streak.

There is another goal, if sixteen in a row couldn't happen, that doesn't mean there aren't still goals to shot for. In Azeri's case it's Spain."

"They want her to race in Europe?"

I'm glad my ignorance was so amusing to Leonard. It seemed every time I asked a question or even let a sound out of my mouth, the next thing I would here was Leonard laughing. It was enough to give a guy a complex.

"No, not the country; the horse."

"What horse?" I asked.

"Spain, of course."

Right before I asked 'who was on first', I realized what Leonard must have meant.

"Oh, Spain, the horse!"

The Dream Race

"Yeah, I won't even ask what you thought I meant," sparing me any further indignity. "Spain held a record that was within reach of Azeri when her victory streak was over; her team's sights were reset to focus on the mare's money record. Goals are wonderful for making great things happen. They may be only numbers, but they are also targets by which performance is measured. Short of putting two horses on the track against each other, these types of records give the every one something to cheer for. Just as they cheered for Personal Ensign in her quest to be undefeated, the public will get behind a horse like Azeri every time is the opponent. The challenge on the track for Personal Ensign in her final race may have been Winning Colors; the crowd wasn't against the Derby winner. Just as the crowd isn't against Spain versus Azeri; no, the public gets the itch, too"

"The itch, that's twice now you mentioned the itch?" I interrupted.

"Yeah, the itch; it's the anticipation of the rare moment when you're close enough to smell history. It smelt like a fine cigar to Jerry Bailey when he approached the record of sixteen straight wins on Cigar. I'm sure it smelt like a sweet perfume to Smith when Azeri won her tenth race in a row. Not many fillies have put together a double digit win streak." The old man sat back in his chair, took a deep whiff of his coffee before finishing the sip.

"The itch and the smell, huh?"

"That's right, it's not just about what you see at the track. Every sense gets stimulated at the track. That's racing and that's the Dream Distaff where the first rule etiquette is ladies first. Of course these ladies have kind of gotten use to being first."

Leonard sat back in his chair and looked at this watch. "Well, boy we can sit here all day talking about horses or we can go see some. You want to head out and see some horses?"

It was like being asked if I wanted to go to Yankee Stadium and watch some of the guys take batting practice. A better comparison might be going to meet the ball players with Mel Allen, the legendary Yankee announcer who had seen them all. Mel and Leonard had something in common; they knew all the stories and shared a love for their respective sports. Each contributed a voice to history. Leonard had a

lifetime of experience to share with someone who could take these stories to a new generation. His words were like reels of old black and white film in some dusty storage trunk. His words took me back in time. I'll never meet Mel Allen. He's gone now; maybe he's watching the Dream Distaff. Luckily, through Leonard I'd gotten to know Regret and the great ladies who have followed in her foot steps.

Leonard opened the door for me as we started to leave Memaw's. "Ladies First" he said, stopping me in my tracks. I gave him a quick look of objection, while taking his ribbing in stride. "The Dream Distaff, that's what I'm talkin' about. Son, you gotta remember 'Ladies First' is more than etiquette; it's the best way to start a day at the races."

The Dream Race

Between Crowns: In 1948 Citation won the Triple Crown. It would be another 25 years before Secretariat would win the next Triple Crown. The period 'between the crowns' from '48 to '73 was filled with stories of classic rivalries, heartbreak, and near misses; but most of all, it was a golden age for racing.

Between Crowns

Breakfast was over and I'd heard about the first of Leonard's Dream Races. It was entertaining, but it didn't answer the question about who was the horse I needed to write

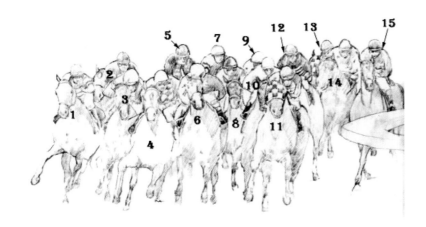

Between Crowns

1. Citation
2. Round Table
3. Bold Ruler
4. Native Dancer
5. Buckpasser
6. Northern Dancer
7. Tim Tam
8. Dr. Fager
9. Damascus
10. Kelso
11. Secretariat
12. Majestic Prince
13. Riva Ridge
14. Nashua
15. Swaps

about. I didn't get up at four-something in the morning to talk about stuff that wasn't going to help me with my article. We made it outside. We had come in separate cars. Mine was the same clunker that got me through college; his was a truck that had gotten him through more, much more. From the looks of it, it could have been his first vehicle. If Leonard was old, then his truck was ancient.

"Let's take my truck down to the farm. I'll bring you back later."

Leonard closed the driver-side door. I slammed mine, thinking I'd have to on such an old truck, but it closed easily. I realized this truck was cared for by a man who paid attention to the details, just like the stories he told. He observed everything, even the minor things. He was from a time when the little things in life were regarded as treasures. I politely opened the truck door again and this time closed it as if closing the door on a Rolls Royce. Leonard looked at me strangely at first. Then he nodded, he knew that I was making an effort to understand.

The drive was barely under way, when we were back at the topic of the Dream Race. We talked or more accurately, I listened all the way to the farm. Leonard pulled his truck into a meticulously groomed courtyard beside a glorious building. I followed him into what turned out to be a barn. If it wasn't for all the horses I might have thought we were going into a church; or maybe even an airport. The building was both huge and pristine. Leonard charged in head first like a man with something to do. I lingered like a sinner in the back row. His feet were moving over a brick floor, while mine were growing roots. I could feel my head spin around trying to take it all in. Leonard emerged from a side room pushing an empty wheel barrow. It didn't take me long to figure out that our job was to fill the wheel barrow up; I could even deduce what we would be filling it up with. I looked out a window, what had been an opaque blanket of darkness was thinning into a translucent mist. Daylight was coming. It was probably a good idea I didn't wear my watch. The thought of how early it was coupled with the sight of the wheel barrow could have caused irreversible mental trauma, or at least a little childish whining.

"Well, do you know how to use this or do you need to read the owner's manual?" Leonard said as he held up the pitch fork.

"I must have skipped school that day. I'm a quick learner, why don't you show me how to do it?" I hoped Leonard understood my smart-aleck sense of humor, since he was holding what amounted to a weapon with five rusty points. Imagine the irony of me catching a nasty case of lockjaw.

"Step back, I wouldn't want to get any manure on your shoes." He said as he spit his tobacco inches from my foot. This was going to be a long day, unless I made my escape soon. I was sure my bed would still take me back.

"I appreciate the story about the Dream Distaff with the fabulous fillies, but . . . I'm still having . . . a well . . . a difficult time . . . ah . . ."

"A difficult time speaking?" OK, Leonard either hated me or he was one funny man, the jury was still out.

"Leonard, I don't want to be rude, but . . ."

"Then don't be."

"What?"

"If you don't want to be rude, then don't be. It's just that simple. Say what you mean and stop trying to dress it up. I'm too old for fluff, son."

"OK, fine, Leonard, you have a dozen horses on the list that ran in the 50s and 60s. This was the dry spell of horse racing. There wasn't a Triple Crown winner from '48 with Citation until Secretariat in '73. Why even put any of those horses on the list of greatest horses?"

"Somebody's been doing some reading, but books are just words and a handful of old faded black and white photos.

Hey, I was there. It was in real living color. I saw 'em all and I know what they could do. I touched 'em. I can still smell 'em forty years later better than you can read about them today."

"But, if none of them could dominate the other horses in any given year, how could any of these be considered the greatest of all time?"

"Babe Ruth was considered the greatest baseball player of all-time, but he also held the record for strikeouts for nearly fifty years. The absence of failure isn't the measure of greatest. Winning doesn't mean you've never lost."

"Yeah, but aren't there horses that never lost?"

"Did they run against the best? Being the best also means that you have competed against the best. You seem to put a great deal of emphasis on Triple Crown winners. Did any of them finish undefeated? From '48 to '73 was not a dry spell for horse racing; it was a golden age."

"How can you say that?"

Leonard pointed at the list in my hand. "See that horse." He pointed at a horse's name.

"Native Dancer?"

"Yeah, depending upon how you measure greatness that horse could be the answer to your question."

"Don't you mean Northern Dancer? I know he won the Kentucky Derby and was a great stallion producing lots of winners."

"Yeah, a lot of folks think he was the first dancer, but no. Northern Dancer is a grandson of Native Dancer. One thing's for sure, the grand pappy is in the race, but as the years go by more people seem awed by the grandson." Leonard twisted his chaw to the other side of his mouth. It was a wonderful form of kinetic punctuation.

"Son, there's one thing ya gotta know, the Gray Ghost had one of the best race records ever, but his real legacy is on the track today."

"He didn't win the Kentucky Derby, I looked at a list of winners. He didn't win it."

"True, that was the one race in twenty-two races that he didn't win. He lost by little more than a head as he closed hard at the finish after being mugged in the first turn. After the Derby nobody ever challenged him on the track again. He overpowered all comers for the rest of his career. Northern Dancer did win the Derby as did several other Native Dancers descendents; but boy, as impressive as that is, think about this. The 2003 Kentucky Derby had sixteen entries and every one had Native Dancer in their pedigree. The Derby may be the one and only race the Gray Ghost didn't win, but he's still leaving his mark on it year after year."

"Or haunting it." I said and Leonard nodded. What was this? Did he really agree with me?

"I couldn't have put it any better." Leonard's words were the confirmation I'd hoped for. Leonard pointed to another name on the list; "Kelso: what do you know about him?" Leonard asked.

"Not much . . . actually before you handed me this list, I'd never heard of him."

"Yeah, and with each day that passes there are more and more people like you who haven't and fewer and fewer of those who can remember when Kelso was the darlin' of every race fan across the country."

"Really?"

"Son, he's the only five-time Horse-of-the-Year. Man, it's tough enough to earn that honor once in a lifetime, but to win it five straight years, now that may be the one record you'll never see broken as long as you live. Track records will fall, there'll be more Triple Crown winners, but I don't know that

we will see another horse dominate the competition for as long a time as Kelso did from '60 to '64. Now, that was a horse. His owner, Mrs. DuPont, would ship that horse all over the country. It was a regular stop as the train rolled through the Carolinas on its way back up to Maryland to pick up the old boy and send him on his way. She loved that horse like a pet. No, she love'd him more like family, matter of fact I guess he was. After Kelso was retired, Mrs. DuPont continued to ride him in fox hunts. Can you imagine a horse with that kind of personality?"

"No way." I had no idea what the big deal was, but it seemed important to Leonard, so I played along. I mean what's the big difference between fox hunting and racing anyhow? I guess I had a lot to learn. I was just hoping Leonard didn't know how little I knew, but I was sure he did.

"Boy, I was there the last time Kelso raced. Son, there wasn't a dry eye in the house. You ever heard about Lou Gehrig's farewell speech at Yankee stadium? It's hard to imagine anything could rival that, but I'll tell you as a man standing right there. When they pulled the saddle off his back for the last time, every man at the track took his hat off out of respect. No one said a word, it just happened one by one; and when all the hats were off, so was the hatch on every eye. It was like someone turned on the faucet. In the race game there

is always something to make you laugh and always something to make you cry. Don't ever forget that and don't ever forget about Kelso. He was a great horse."

Leonard turned and walked away. It was his favorite way of closing the story on one horse and moving on to the next contender. I would have to chase him around the barn. His short, little, wiry legs could scoot him out of sight in the blink of an eye. He may have admitted that he cried at the track, but he still never liked for any one to see it.

"A little while ago, you called the years from Citation to Secretariat, a dry spell. Let me tell you why they were really the golden years. I read it from many of the writers who were around back then. Yeah, that's what they called it. But, you know, I like to call it something else. I call it Between Crowns; those golden years between Citation's Triple Crown in '48 and Secretariat's crown in '73. Between Crowns was a remarkable time to be at the track watching the battles of great horses who each seemingly were unbeatable, until they met their equal. There were the great duels between Swaps and Nashua, east coast versus west coast. Swaps was never given any respect back east, not until he beat Nashua, the royalty of the old guard of racing. When those two battled, the other horses had to keep to the side and let them go at it. When

Swaps and Nashua took on each other they didn't need jockeys. I swear those two knew each other before they ever met. It was like they had been reading about each other in the newspaper. They were rivals, but they were more; they loved to race each other. Until they met each other, neither was really pushed. These classic battles say more about this era Between Crowns than any book. There's not been many days at the track better than when Swaps and Nashua locked horns. It was a battle, each race a piece of a bigger war. They were two generals who each respected the other and wanted nothing more than victory. Any one who tells you that a horse doesn't know if he won or not, doesn't know squat about horses. The second they break from the gate they know where the finish line is and when great horses meet, they always know right where the other one is. First thing Nashua would do is look around and find Swaps. The rest of the field was just obstacles and the finish line is where they took care of business."

Leonard stopped to check on a couple of young men mucking stalls. Then, he returned his attention to me.

"Do you believe me, yet? Do you believe that the period Between Crowns was a golden age?"

"Well, I think I understand what you are saying, but a couple of good horses is no way to make up for a Triple Crown winner." The devil's advocate in me was polluting the intelligent side of my brain.

"I see, so you want a horse that wins those three races and nothing else is important."

"Well, not just those three races, but if they can't win at least those three how can we even consider them as the greatest horse of all time?" I still couldn't get over believing only Triple Crown winners should be considered in the discussion.

"Well, I see." The teacher metaphorically folded up his lesson books under his arm to prepare to leave the room. In reality, he bent down and picked up a pitch fork and laid it into a wheel barrow filled with manure. He picked up the handles and started to make his way out of his classroom.

"No, Leonard, I didn't mean only Triple Crown winners would be considered."

Leonard straightened his back. The sight of how slowly and deliberately he moved helped me feel his years of wear and tear. "There were a lot of special horses Between the Crowns; how many of them were great is a different matter altogether and it may be impossible to separate the special ones from the great ones."

Leonard lowered the cart handles and let the light from the barn windows bounce off the top of his head creating a golden halo.

"It wasn't always just two horses that locked horns. Maybe one of the most famous track battles took place in the late 60s when three of the fastest horses ever to blaze their way around the track hooked up."

"Three in the same year?" I was like a kid in the corner wearing a dunce cap and begging to be let back into class.

"Uh-huh, that's right. It was Dr. Fager, the fastest horse at a mile that the track had seen in a hundred years. There was also Buckpasser. His injuries kept him out of all three of the classics, but when he was on the track, he was a monster. The final one of the three musketeers was Damascus. Each of these horses earned Horse-of-the-Year honors during their careers and each did it by beating the other two. It didn't matter how they ran against the world, what mattered was how each did against the other two. They brought out the best in each other."

"Dr. Fager is a funny name, is he named after a real-life doctor?"

"Actually, he is. Legendary trainer, John Nerud took a spill and had a brain clot. Dr. Fager is the brain surgeon who

saved his life. In this business the ultimate compliment is to say thank you by naming a horse after someone. Long after the doctor passed away, his legacy is remembered through track records and babies with wings for legs. The colt wore the red and black checkered silks of Tartan Farms. Dr. Fager created wind as he breezed around the track; all that horse needed was a set of bagpipes to go along with his tartan silks. Dr. Fager put Florida racing on the map like no other horse. He even got a speeding ticket when his van crossed the state line on his way back to Florida. It was staged for the newspaper back at a time when the news could still be fun. Yes sir, that horse gave Florida-breds the respect it had lacked. Even the Triple Crown winner Affirmed didn't do for Florida horses what that tall bolt of lightning did."

"Wind and lightning, uh? Maybe they should have called him Tempest. What about the other two?"

"Buckpasser was another in the line of solid horses coming out of the stables of Ogden Phillips. His pedigree read like a who's who of thoroughbred royalty. His sire was Tom Fool, a great horse in his own right and he was out of a War Admiral daughter. There just aren't many horses with big wins and Triple Crowns in their blood like Buckpasser. When he was healthy he was unbeatable. Damascus and Dr. Fager each had a glimpse to see just how good he was. I saw it with my own eyes. When I think of greatness, I can only imagine what could have been. His babies have carried the torch in his name and showed the promise he had; but one thing is for sure, when he was right, it wouldn't take long before he was out of sight."

"And Damascus?" That's all I had to say to make Leonard's face turn into the stream of light coming in through the barn window. His dark skin began to glow as he squinted looking into the sun as if looking fondly into the past.

"He was the fastest to wear the red polka dots of Belair Stud. Gallant Fox and Omaha both won Triple Crowns for Belair. Nashua wore the regal Belair colors. But, none of them ever ran against Damascus. It was one thing to win at the track; it was something else to be the fastest horse ever to wear the famous polka-dot silks. His hooves were like the wings on Mercury's feet. His farrier wasn't a blacksmith; he was an aerospace engineer. That horse had a rocket under his saddle. I could remember standing at the edge of the track and trying to see through the flying dirt as it bounced off his belly. I was trying to see his legs. They were only a blur. I swear he never touched the ground."

"A blur?"

The Dream Race

"Yeah, that's right; a blur. But, there's one thing that's perfectly clear; any one of these three could have been the greatest of all-time, if they didn't have to race each other. Old men like me, may not be able to pick the better of the three; but what would have been better for racing: one great horse or the best three horse rivalry in the history of racing? It was something special the day all three of them took the track at the same time. It was as thrilling as the Belmont when the crown's on the line. Everyone says they want a Triple Crown, but inside what everyone really wants is a great race, the kind that makes your skin prickle up and down your arm. From the moment these three entered the starting gate to every time I remember it now; that is exactly what happened, a moment that lives forever in the memory."

Leonard soaked in another face-load of sunlight, then quickly moved his wheel barrow to a new spot on the stage. He was like a Shakespearean actor, hitting his cues and delivering his lines perfectly.

"Majestic Prince, now that was a horse and the whole world knew it. That horse has since received less attention for a horse deserving so much more. I think it was all because the expectations were set so high. This horse was supposed to win and never lose. This horse was supposed to win the Triple Crown and never taste defeat. Anything less and his career would be considered a failure. Impossible expectations? Absolutely. Is it the truth? Absolutely."

I didn't say a word. I knew nothing about this Majestic Prince, yet Leonard spoke with the kind of praise you would expect to hear when describing the best, the very best. From greatness to anonymity was one of the oldest forms of paradox.

"Hall-of-Fame jockey Johnny Longden moved out of the saddle to become a trainer. When he saw Majestic Prince, he was sure this was the horse that had it all. When Longden pushed the bid to $250,000; the price set a record and the auction made shockwaves. After that, the bar of expectations was set higher for Majestic Prince than any horse before or since. In '69 when Majestic Prince won the Derby, it made Longden the only man to ride a Derby winner and train another. This Native Dancer grandson made the old gray ghost proud as his progeny continued to haunt Churchill Downs. A month later, Majestic Prince was the first horse to go to the post in the Belmont Stakes undefeated. That's right, he won the Derby and the Preakness and every race before that including his entire 2-year old season. Longden told me he didn't want to take him through the mile and a half at Belmont, but there was pressure to go for the crown. He came in second to Arts and Letters that day, and that one loss wasn't just a defeat; it was the end of his immortality. He wasn't a god, he

was just another great horse; but that wasn't good enough. People blamed the horse for not being perfect. He took on all challengers and beat them all, but perfection was what had been expected. It didn't matter that he produced dozens upon dozens of stakes winners. Majestic Prince was destined for greatness and the adoring public soon became the forgetting public. Boy, I'll tell you this; that horse was great. Ten times out and nine times first, by any standard that was greatness; but when people are hungry for one thing, sometimes they'll starve before they'll eat something else."

Leonard moved to the next stall. He shifted around until he found the exact spot where the sunshine was again his limelight.

"Imagine hundreds of years, thousands if not millions of foals being born all over the world; what is the likelihood that two horses worthy of this discussion would actually be born on the same day and on the same farm?"

"I don't know, a million to one?"

"Maybe a billion to one . . . unless that one place happens to be Claiborne Farm and the two horses happen to be Bold Ruler and Round Table."

"Seriously? Cool."

"You got that right. Cool."

"Bold who and what kind of table?"

"Bold Ruler and Round Table; they were born the same night. Round Table's sire was Princequillo who may be better known as the dam sire of the great Secretariat."

"The damn sire?"

"Not the damn sire, but the dam sire."

"Yeah, Leonard isn't that what I said?"

"Boy, sometimes I wonder if you know anything about horses."

"Hey, I'm not the expert; but didn't you say the damn horse."

"Before you make a dang fool of yourself I better straighten you out."

"Leonard, don't you mean, a damn fool?" I didn't get the laugh out of him that I'd expected.

"Dam is the term used for the mare, you know . . . a horse's mother. So, when I say Princequillo was the dam sire that means he was the father of the mother of a particular horse. In this case the horse is Secretariat. Who just so happens to have been sired . . . fathered by . . . Bold Ruler."

The Dream Race

"Cool, so what you are saying is that these two horses were born the same day on the same farm; and later one of them would father one of the greatest horses of all-time out of the other one's sister. Right?"

"I am amazed."

"See, Leonard, I've been listening to your whole dam story." I winked and he smiled.

"Miracles never cease."

"So, tell me more about these farm buddies; Bold Ruler and Round Table. Were either ever really famous?"

"They didn't run head-to-head that often, but when they did it was as if they were back on the farm playin' in the paddock. Horses never forget. You can wean 'em, but they never forget where they learned to run. I think when a horse takes his first run through the fields; it's like when you get your first kiss. Say whatever you want, but you never forget it. You may never talk about it, years may go by without thinkin' about it, but trust me, boy, you never forget it."

"So, who was yours?"

"Young man, if you're gonna test me, you're gonna have to do better than that. Her name was Thelma, she was cuter than a lady bug. That's what I called her. We were all of ten years old, but we both knew we were all grown up. It was after church. I had about ten minutes before I had to be back at the track to breeze a couple of horses. That kiss lasted all of ten seconds and it's lasted the eighty years since. Like I said, you never forget."

"Just like Bold Ruler and Round Table."

"Boy, you may not be the sharpest tool in the shed, but with a little work you can cut through anything." Leonard smiled as he delivered his back-handed compliment.

"Other than the fact they were born on the same day, what really makes them famous?"

"When your most famous son's name is Secretariat, that alone is plenty; but that didn't help him win the '57 Horse-of-the-Year honors in one of the deepest crops of race horses in any year. As for Round Table, his forty-three wins is still a standard other horses are measured by. He was a locomotive, just chugging along year after year, race after race. Some will tell you, longevity is one mark of the greatest horse of all-time."

"Round Table, uh?"

"That's right." Leonard again hoisted the handles on the wheel barrow and made his way to the next stall. The sun was a little higher. The golden light was highlighting his hands

as he held the pitch fork like Excalibur. "Yeah, Round Table; what else would you expect from a horse whose father's name was Princequillo and Knight's Daughter was the name of his mother."

"Dam."

"You can say that again." Leonard flashed his infectious smile as he spun the pitch fork around in his hands. I don't know why I did what I did next, but I reached out and took the pitch fork out of his hands and without any coaching I began to pick through the straw to find the little nuggets Leonard had been plucking out. I filtered the chips of wood shavings as much as possible, leaving the wood behind and only taking out the bad apples.

"It's kind of calming isn't it?" Leonard said as he watched.

"Yes, I guess, but I wouldn't want to make a habit of it."

"Why's that?" Leonard asked as he reached for the pitchfork; which for some reason I declined to hand back to him.

"No disrespect, but doesn't this get boring after a while, not to mention the smell."

"Well, since you just did mention the smell, let's start there. After a while you begin to recognize that smell. It ain't what you think."

"It's not? Then what is it?"

"Boy, breathe in. Got a good whiff of that? Now, that right there is the smell of money and don't let any one ever try to tell you otherwise."

I coughed as I may have gotten choked on some spare change.

"And as for being bored, this is like fishing or playing chess. It's the best time to let the mind wander. Fishing's not about the fish. It's about all the things you think about when you ain't thinkin' 'bout nothin'."

Leonard used language the way an artist uses a brush. His country grammar would come and go to better paint his picture. He was as articulate as he wanted to be. Ain't was a bright color on his palette and he used it for highlights when he knew it worked best. I dug back into the shavings to clean some more. "And it ain't bad exercise." I said as I copied his smile.

"Boy, they have been trying to take my pitch fork away for almost twenty years. They just don't get it; to me it ain't work. If that's all it was, I would have quit years ago. Just being around these beasts is reward enough; but please don't tell any one, 'cause it's kinda nice to get paid to be here. If I had to, I'd pay them to do it. Son, don't think I'm here for the money. I got more money than I'll ever need. What I need now, is an answer to the Dream Race. That is what I think about when my mind is free to wander."

"Is that all the horses you would have in a race Between Crowns?"

"No, there's a couple more. The first of which is Tim Tam. He raced for the famed Calumet Farm. They gave us two Triple Crown winners including Citation in '48 and plenty of close calls. Calumet could have had several horses in the field between crowns. Mr. Wright's Calumet was a machine that produced one champion after another. I see TimTam in this race because he was the closet to being Calumet's third Triple Crown winner. He won the first two legs of the Triple Crown and was favored to win the Belmont. He actually broke a leg in the race; he finished, but any hope of being immortalized was also finished."

"Even, as little as I know, I guess Calumet has to have a representative during these years."

"True, just so long as that isn't a slight to any of Tim Tam's talent. Don't put him in the race because he carries the devil red colors of Calumet; put him in the race because he earned it."

"Leonard, is there anyone else between Citation and Secretariat?"

"Oh, yeah. The last link in the chain and certainly not the least. He was a glimpse into the future as he wore the same silks and blinkers that would be made famous a year later by his stable mate. They were the blue and white checkered silks of Mr. Chenery. The horse was Riva Ridge. He collected the first jewels of the Triple Crown, but fell in the Belmont. He was supposed to be the horse that would finally give his ailing owner his first Triple Crown. Riva Ridge was on the cover of all the sports magazines. This horse was going to be the happy ending to a life long career breeding and racing horses for Mr. Chenery. By the end of the '72 racing season, Mr. Chenery did in fact own the Horse-of-the-Year, but it was his two-year old, that big red horse named Secretariat. Mr. Chenery died before the following season. Riva Ridge came as close to the crown as Mr. Chenery would get in his lifetime, but his daughter continued his racing dream the following season. Miss Penny was the delight of the racing industry and their big red horse took the blue and white checkers to all the places where Riva

Ridge had come so close. It was one of the most amazing back to back runs of success by one stable and Mr. Chenery had to watch it all from heaven; but as I have said before, the Dream Race is run in heaven and you can bet Mr. Chenery was right there cheering those blue and white silks."

Leonard took the pitch fork from my hands. He looked into my eyes. "Son, do yourself a favor and never talk about those years as being a dry spell. It was the golden age of racing with passionate owners, charismatic jockeys, and horses that fought every step of the way. These horses never faded on the track the way time has faded the memory of their accomplishments. The feats haven't faded, just the memory of them. Newspapers turn yellow with time and the black and white photos are a dull brown, but the memories are crystal clear and in vivid color. I can hear the pounding of their hooves shaking the ground as they race past. My heart starts pounding like a drum as their pace quickens down the backstretch. . . . oh, in case you're still wondering who wins. We all do."

The Dream Race

Superfreaks: The 1970's saw the end of the Triple Crown drought as not just one horse won the crown, but three horses won the Triple Crown in a decade that produced some of the greatest horses the track has ever seen.

Superfreaks

The one thing I was beginning to realize about Leonard was that he was the perfect blend of a romantic soul, a photographic memory, and the intelligence of the fastest computer. His stories were works of art; cinematography through words. I could close my eyes and see the bright colors, hear the sounds, and feel the excitement. His conviction was comparable to the great orators of the ages as he meshed fact and folklore.

There was something he wanted to say, but he didn't.

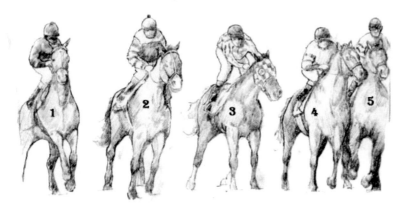

Superfreaks!

1. Spectacular Bid
2. Seattle Slew
3. Secretariat
4. Affirmed
5. Alydar

Much later I realized he was thanking me. To him, I was the one doing him the favor. Just by asking the questions and listening to his story of the Dream Race; I was doing for him what he was doing for me. I've come to realize that going to the track is something you can do alone, but it's more fun to go with some one else. That goes for the Dream Race as well. Leonard had been there hundreds of times, but this was a rare treat for him to take some one with him.

"You know, the Florida Derby was one of the best ways to determine who's the early favorite for the Kentucky Derby. Some good horses came out of California back then; but over the years, if you study the records it was pretty common for the winner of the Florida Derby or the Flamingo Stakes to be the favorite come Kentucky Derby time. Those top horses came from Kentucky, New York, Maryland; but they came through Florida and that meant Hialeah. Today, Gulfstream runs the Florida Derby, but as much as you can try you just can't create nostalgia. No sir, can't do it. Don't get me wrong, I love Gulfstream, but it ain't Hialeah and if Gulfstream could talk, it would say as much. Those two tracks are so different, like night and day. Each was the perfect complement for the other, but it doesn't matter now 'cause it's the sunshine of Gulfstream versus the daylight of Calder now; the romance of the night is gone."

"Leonard, come on a horse track is a horse track." I must have been trying to antagonize him, but he stayed cool as he explained what he meant.

"Hialeah was like going to a black tie affair with everybody in tuxedoes."

"They wore tuxedoes to the race track?"

"It's a metaphor; please tell me they taught you that in college."

"Oh, a metaphor, so they didn't really . . . oh, sorry, go on," Nothing worse than having to pull your own foot from your mouth to get your spanking.

"Gulfstream trades in the tuxedoes for lots of bright colors. Gulfstream belongs to a different generation."

"Tell me more."

"Do you like disco music?" Leonard was the master of the unexpected question.

"What? Disco music . . . well, uh", I really didn't want to hurt his feelings. He must have had a point, but in one breath he was talking about Tuxedoes in Miami and in the next he's asking me if I liked disco music. No offense, but where I came from you had a better chance of finding some one who liked the flu.

"You know, the 70s were the age of disco. Even the Rolling Stones had a disco sound in the 70s and of course, Saturday Night Fever was the rage."

"Well, I wasn't born until after the 70s so I guess that let's me out."

"Yeah, that's too bad 'cause while the world was shaking its booty, the horse world was spoiled year after year by some of the greatest horses ever to break from the gate."

As we moved through the barn Leonard reached over to an old radio, or at least that's what I think it was, covered in a century of barn dust. I know radios hadn't been around for a hundred years, but this one was collecting dust long before guys like Marconi and Tesla did their magic. To my surprise it wasn't a radio. It was some form of an ancient boom box. Leonard pulled out a huge tape. It was like a cassette tape on steroids, nearly five times larger than anything I had seen before.

"Ya can't get these any more," Leonard said as he pushed one of the mammoth tapes into the box. The music

came on with a funky beat and wasn't too different from what we dance to down at the clubs. "Eight tracks"

I had heard of eight tracks before, it was like hearing about the dinosaurs. We had to believe they existed for no other reason than the fact that our parents told us they were real; but no one I knew had ever seen one.

"So, that's an 8-track?"

"Son, I know a little something about CDs and DVDs, but I bet you know nothing about this stuff. See, that's the difference between young and old. Old folks know what you know, you just think we don't and the young people don't know the first thing about what we know. It's the same way on the track." Leonard took a moment to do some rump-hump bumping to the 8-track's music. "Superfreaky" Leonard sang along, then said, "I'm not here to preach, but take a moment to go back to the 70s. Think about what was going on in the world and maybe you can begin to see why a horse helped saved America. Is that over dramatic? Only if you look at things from your twenty-first century perspective; but if you let yourself go back in time to the 70s you just may get the picture. Imagine you have a choice of listening to this boom box or the news. You see, I have the choice to put this tape in and hear

what I want or I can listen to the radio with every one talking about the war in Vietnam or Watergate. You probably have no idea what Watergate is." Leonard returned to his singing, "Superfreaky".

"It was the hotel where the Democratic Party was during the political convention before the '72 election. There was a break in which the Republicans covered up and ultimately led to the resignation of President Nixon."

"I'm impressed; do you know that most kids your age have no idea what Watergate was?"

"I only know it because we talked about it in school."

"Imagine every time you turned on the radio all you heard was negative. It was a demoralizing time; but this little boom box and millions just like it gave Americans a chance to say I have had enough bad news. You see, humans are like horses – we get along much better if you feed us stuff that is good for us." Leonard reached down into a large tub filled with a sticky grain. "Good for the body," he said as he poured a handful of grain into my left hand. He then stuck the 8-track tape back into my right hand, "Good for the soul." With that Leonard began to perform his bumping boogie again. Even the horses came over to their stall doors to watch him.

The Dream Race

"And what has all this disco dancing got to do with horse racing?"

"Nothing, if a horse doesn't come along that does the same thing as this music; a horse that makes people feel good about themselves, a horse that makes people want to listen to the news, watch television, and in short be proud again. We are a proud people and when we aren't, there's something wrong. It was a horse that came along and restored the faith of Americans that life wasn't all bad. Just when we were about to stop trusting people, it was a horse that came along and showed us how to live again; and that horse was Secretariat."

"Now, that's one I've heard of."

"He was a great horse, but he also came from an era that seemed to give one great horse after another. Each year during the 70s there seemed to a special horse that would rise up and separate himself from the rest. The magazines put a horse on the cover, television covered the sport like never before. Not since the days of radio had mass media been infatuated with racing. It really was a phenomenon. This country has always turned to its athletes as heroes and never more than when the country was in need of some one to look up to. It just so happened this time, it was a horse. Once the world started watching Secretariat it couldn't get enough of horses on television. By the end of the 70s disco music was falling out of favor, but not until it served its purpose. The same was true of horse racing. Television brought millions of fans, but most of all the 70s brought a few great champions the likes of which we haven't seen since."

Leonard reached up to the tape player and turned off the music, then he walked towards the other end of the barn leaving me to chase after him.

"Like who?"

"How about three Triple Crown winners and two or three more with greatest within their grasps?"

"Twenty-five years without a Triple Crown winner and then three in one decade."

"Three in six years to be exact. On the heels of Secretariat came Seattle Slew and Affirmed. It's impossible to talk about Affirmed being the last Triple Crown winner without talking about the horse that may have won the crown in any other year."

"How's that? Weren't there a lot of horses that came close, winning two legs of the crown?"

"Yeah, that's true. There have been several horses who came close that way, but none that have come close the way Alydar did."

"Alydar?"

"Alydar and Affirmed or Affirmed and Alydar, either way it's hard to say one without mentioning the other. Today, history remembers both of them, almost like they were one. I guess history is a funny thing, over time Affirmed will be remembered and Alydar may drift away. That would be unfortunate, because these two combined to be racing's greatest rivalry, dueling it out every time they met. While Affirmed was winning all three legs of the Triple Crown, to be the eleventh horse to do so; Alydar was doing something no other horse has done. Alydar came in second in all three Triple Crown races to the same horse."

"Affirmed, right?" I knew it was a dumb question, but it came out before I could latch my lips.

"Real good, college boy, did you figure that one out all by yourself?" Leonard said with a friendly pat on the back. "Affirmed and Alydar wrote a page in history as they crossed the finish line at Belmont together. Affirmed won by a head, but the question has been asked over and over again, what if;

what if Alydar had run in any other year. If not for Affirmed would Alydar have won the Triple Crown? If Affirmed is in this Dream Race, then Alydar is too and he's right beside Affirmed. It would be tough to say who's the greatest of all-time; but if Affirmed claimed the title, then it's only logical Alydar would have to finish second."

"Amazing "

"The story is even more amazing when you see a parallel to the story of David and Goliath. Alydar was a blue blood from the elite Calumet Farm; the giant of racing. Mr. Wright built a dynasty at Calumet. After Mr. Wright passed away his widow, Mrs. Markey, took over running the farm. After years in the shadow of Calumet's former greatness, Alydar was supposed to return the farm to the pinnacle of racing. Now, compare that to Affirmed. Nobody knew him as a weanling. He came from a little known Florida farm. No Florida horse had ever won a Triple Crown. None had even won a classic before Needles in the 50s."

"Really, I thought Florida was supposed to be right behind Kentucky with its horses."

"Not that close, but closer than they use to be. You have to keep in mind, the horses running and winning in

The Dream Race

Florida for many years were just tourists. They come down for the winter and head back up when it got warmer."

"I've heard of snowbirds, but now you're telling me there are snowhorses, too."

"What I'm telling you is that before Affirmed, Florida-breds weren't given much consideration against the big Kentucky farms and their top horses. When a good Florida horse came along, it was more chance than years of selective breeding of great stallions to great mares. When the '78 season started, Alydar was the giant and Affirmed was considered a good horse with a small, but loyal fan club. By the end of the Belmont Stakes to call Affirmed 'just a good horse' would be one of the biggest understatements of all time. To this day the jockeys have become as legendary as their battles. Stevie Cauthen was a 17-year-old that rode with fearless energy on Affirmed, while Alydar was ridden by another rising star, Jorge Velazquez. Despite long successful riding careers, the summer of '78 has to be a highlight for both of them."

"What else happened on the track in the 70s?"

"The two years before Secretariat came along there were a couple of near misses with Canenero and then Riva Ridge. Each pulled down the first two classics, but neither lived up to their cover stories on Sports Illustrated. However, the public was beginning to get interested in racing again as it had back before the Second World War. This may be hard to believe, but there was a time when horse racing was bigger than any professional sport; the only thing that could give it a run for its money was baseball or boxing. When the horses were running the crowds would fill the tracks, hundreds of thousands of people. The early 70s started a new trend and when Secretariat came along; he wasn't just the second coming of Big Red; he was the salvation and the future of racing."

"Amen." I wasn't sure why I said that, but sometimes when Leonard gets the pulpit warmed up, the preacher in him comes out and the track becomes his church. Then, again; maybe the devil made me do it.

"Twenty-five years since Citation ran the table and it was over fifty years since the original Big Red, Man o' War, ruled the track. It takes a dynamic horse to be mentioned in the same breath, much less carry the same nickname. Secretariat had the heart and the performances to go along with it. There was no bigger show than his Belmont victory over thirty lengths in front of the second place horse. The Crown was on his head by the time he came out of the final turn. The

backstretch was more like a curtain call with the crowd standing and cheering."

"Thirty lengths."

"Oh, yeah, I can still see the looks on people's faces. Most of them had tears in their eyes as they watched Secretariat run away from the field. He turned unbelievable times at each pole. By the end of the race, if you could still call it that; the question was whether there had been or ever would be another performance on the track to equal what we were seeing. It wasn't just a great moment in racing, it was one of the greatest moments of all sports. This moment in racing has been compared to Hank Aaron breaking Babe Ruth's home run record. Both happened within a year of the other. Records and feats that were expected to last forever fell right before the eyes of every one at the track and by television, all over the world. Secretariat gave racing and horse breeders everywhere something to cheer for. Break out the disco music, 'cause Secretariat just made his grandma proud."

"Secretariat's grandma? Are you just being funny?"

"No, just tying up some loose pieces of information, like Secretariat's grandmother's name just happens to be Miss Disco. Imagine that, she was born in 1944, long before

anybody every thought about shaking their booty, disco music, or a big red chestnut on the cover of TIME magazine."
Leonard busted out one more bar of, "Superfreak, superfreak, superfreaky."

"Now, I think I've heard everything."

"Boy, the 70s were just getting started when Secretariat dominated the track. It would be a couple years later when Baby Huey took over."

"Baby Huey?"

"I keep forgetting how young you are. There use to be a kid's cartoon called Baby Huey. It was a baby duck that wore a diaper all the time. This baby duck was huge and strong as an ox. Well, that's where the nickname came from. Baby Huey was a black-bay colt bought at auction for only $17,500; not a bad investment when you consider it's been estimated he made his owners over $100 million dollars."

"A hundred million dollars!!"

"Uh huh, not bad for a horse nicknamed after a comic strip. At first he was a little clumsy, but once he got on the track he was unbeatable. This big colt grew into himself and out grew the competition."

The Dream Race

"So, the 70s gave us Secretariat, Seattle Slew, and Affirmed along with Alydar, Riva Ridge, and Canerero." I summarized the list I was compiling.

"Remember, you can't talk about the best horses from the seventy's without including the filly, Ruffian. Even though she's in the Dream Distaff, she certainly deserved to be mentioned in the same breath as any horse from the seventies."

"Even the Triple Crown winners?"

"Most definitely, look at her times and what she did on the track. Her legacy has become the tragedy that ended her life, I think you know how I feel about her loss. I think it's racing history that will get short changed. Ruffian will be famous because of the way her life ended as opposed to the way she lived. Yes sir, she could hand with any horse from her era or any other for that matter." Leonard wasn't smiling and that in itself was a rarity. Before I could say anything, Leonard spit and added another horse.

"Exceller needs to be at least given some consideration during this time. He was champion in Europe and he was more of an after thought when he was entered in the Jockey Club Gold Cup. You see, he was an after thought 'cause the whole world was watching just two horses. Seattle Slew and Affirmed were going to be the first Triple Crown winners to square off on the track. The race seemed to be a easy victory for Slew, until Exceller came charging back from over twenty lengths to become the only horse ever to beat two Triple Crown winners and he did it in the same race. Now, you can't leave a horse like that off your list, now can ya?"

"No, I guess not. Now, do I have the complete list?"

"You'll have the whole list when you add one more spectacular horse."

"Who's that?"

"Maybe the best of them all was Spectacular Bid. The Bid was a steel gray horse who turned snow white in his later years. He was one of the most dominating horses ever to set foot onto the track. Willie 'The Shoe' Shoemaker, rode the Bid. Spectacular Bid was going to be the one that Shoe would finally win his Triple Crown on. The Bid crushed all comers in the first two legs of the Triple Crown and was a 1 to 4 favorite up until the day of the Belmont. It was the morning of the Belmont when one of the great mysteries of racing occurred. When the groom came to feed him on the day the Bid was supposed to go down in history, a problem was discovered; one

that would mean he would go down in defeat instead of history."

"What was it?"

"A safety pin" Leonard answered.

"A safety pin?"

"That's right, a safety pin shoved all the way into his hoof and rumors of how it got there have run rabid every since."

"What?"

"Oh yeah, it was the day of the biggest race of Spectacular Bid's career. It should have been the third straight Triple Crown winner in three years. Instead, the heavily favored Bid who would have been scratched under any other circumstances raced on guts and three good legs. Even Pegasus needs all four legs to fly, it was beyond all hope for the Bid to win, but that's horse racing. There ain't a church around with more hope than the race track. There's probably as much prayin' in the grandstand as there is in the church pews."

"And a whole lot more swearing" prompting Leonard's one word reply.

"Amen." Leonard sang along again, "Superfreak, superfreak . . . you know that's just what those horses from the 70s were; Secretariat, Slew, Affirmed, and even the Bid and Alydar – they were super freaks."

We had made it from one end of the race barn to the other and back again. Leonard replaced the tape in the boom box and turned up the volume. The new funky music had a rhythmic beat with a sexy disco-diva singing, 'Ring My Bell'. It was the perfect song as I pictured the stars of the 70s breaking from the gate at Gulfstream as the track announcer called out, 'They're off!'"

"What, no tuxedoes?"

"Polyester, baby; bright and flashy, loud and outrageous. Throw in some platform shoes and that, young man, is superfreaky."

The Dream Race

The Three Kings: Today, every thoroughbred's ancestry can be traced back to at least one of three Arabian stallions. These foundation horses were brought to England over three hundred years ago from all over Europe, Africa, and the Middle East.

The Three Kings

I wasn't sure how good Leonard's ears were, but I was sure he heard my stomach growling. It had been several hours, or if you were to ask my stomach, a lifetime since we had eaten last.

"Tea time," Leonard said as he signaled with a sipping motion complete with his little pinky held delicately away from his imaginary cup.

"Tea time?" As far as I was concerned, he could call it

Three Kings

1. Darley Arabian
2. Byerly Turk
3. Godolphin Barb

anything he wanted as long as it meant food was in the near-to-immediate future as defined by seconds and not minutes.

"Yeah, that's what time it is in England right about now, tea time."

It was a pattern; Leonard was on another of his missions to confuse the obvious with some obscure reference, then he'd segue to the intended topic of discussion.

"Hey, man, as long as you throw in a fistful of crumpets, I'm game."

"Son, do you even know what a crumpet is?"

"No, but I'm sure it's something to eat, right?"

"Yeah, it's kind of a cross between a cracker and a cookie," Leonard said.

"I don't care if it's a cross between a rock and stick; if it's edible, give me a fistful of those bad boys."

Leonard smiled. "Good, 'cause I was just gonna give you a bucket of oats, but I could toss a couple rocks in if you'd like."

"Stop it! You're only making me hungrier. Let's eat."

The Dream Race

"Alright, alright . . . you've put in a good morning's work, let's eat. You did bring your lunch, right?" Leonard's question was news to me. I was starving to death and he was feeding me a bunch of what we'd been mucking all morning.

"Yeah, old buddy, it's in my car back at the restaurant."

"Well, if we have to go back and get it, we might as well eat there." Leonard winked, squeezed the back of my neck, and steered me towards the door. Now, I'm not exactly tall, but he had to be walking on his tippy-toes as he led me out of the barn.

"So, why Tea time?" I asked.

"Come again."

"Tea Time, why Tea Time, it's not like you to mention something like that for no reason."

"Boy, you just might make a good newspaper reporter after all. Did you know all thoroughbreds can be traced back to England?"

"Wait a minute. Are you saying every horse in this country traces its roots back to England?"

"Well, to be exact, no; not every horse. There were wild horses out west when this land was discovered. Besides, I didn't say every horse, I said every thoroughbred."

"Leonard, so what you're saying is that all thoroughbreds come from England."

"Boy, I'm gonna go one step farther than that; every thoroughbred around the world can be traced back not just to England, but back to one of three different stallions."

"You can't be serious. What's the catch?"

"The only catch here is the first of the three stallions. He was brought back to England after being taken as a war prize from one of the crusades. You have to admit, that's quite a catch. I guess if we're gonna have a whole day of racing in heaven, one of those races should be the three foundation stallions."

"I guess over tea, you can tell me the whole story of the three foundation stallions. First, let me ask you a question. Where would they race?" I asked.

"It could be at Epsom Downs. It's just outside London in an area called Surrey. The Epsom Derby has been run there for well over two-hundred years and it was the model Colonel Clark used when he set up the Kentucky Derby at Churchill Downs. The whole world tends to agree that the Derby is the most famous race in the world. The only debate seems to be whether it's the

Epsom of the Kentucky Derby they're talking about, but I have another place in mind. I'll tell you about it in a minute."

"I've never heard of the Epsom Derby."

"I guess that lets us know which side of the pond you come from and which side of the debate you take."

"Go on, Leonard."

"Well, horse racing in England has a deep history. I can tell you, I've learned more about racing from a couple of chatty Brits in a few hours than talking to most Americans who fancy themselves as being race experts. I'm sure they feel we've taken something precious from them and the funny thing is most Americans don't even know we've taken anything. Most Americans just think horse racing started in the states and spread everywhere else."

"Like Basketball."

"Yeah, that's what we think; but in reality, it's more like football, soccer, or baseball. All are games derived from some other international sport. Horse racing is a way of life in England and goes deeper into who they are as a culture than we can imagine. Over here, we just bet on 'em and read about 'em in the news if they win the Triple Crown. Over there, they talk about 'em the way we talk about our sports heroes; but that is the way it's gone on for over three hundred years and the

automobile won't change the Brits and their love of all equestrian sporting events. If it has a horse in it, the English love it."

"I still can't get over the thought that every thoroughbred can be traced back to three stallions."

"Three hundred years and every pedigree out there goes back to at least one of these three stallions."

"Well, if these weren't thoroughbreds yet, what were they?" I asked.

"All three of these foundation stallions were Arabians."

"Arabians . . ."

"They are one of the oldest breeds of horses. They are known more for their beauty than for their athletic ability; but don't be fooled, those pretty little horses can run all day. Their small size helped them with endurance."

"How small?"

"At that time they were only about 13 – 14 hands."

"Compared to . . ."

The Dream Race

"Well, the draft horses were often 17 to 18 hands; which means I could almost walk under a draft horse's belly and not have to take my hat off and I could look across the back of an Arab."

"They must have been a funny sight."

"Maybe, but they're too beautiful to be funny and they were too athletic to be seen as just a pretty horse."

"Leonard, let me get this straight; there were three horses some place in England and every horse was bred to one of them."

"No, actually it wasn't that way at all, but I'll explain that in a minute. Besides, I thought you were the one dumb with hunger."

Leonard was right, I had during the course of our conversation forgotten about being hungry. I don't know if it was Leonard's reminder or the smell blowing out of the little diner, but I was suddenly hungrier than ever. Once we settled at a table, Leonard picked up where he'd left off.

"Hard to think of all these thoroughbreds coming from three Arabians; yeah, it kind of blows the mind," Leonard said. I knew he was getting ready to tell one of his stories; so, I quickly ordered, sat back, and got comfortable.

"Son, didn't you say you were related to Mark Twain?" I knew I never told Leonard that. He must have heard it from someone else. It had to have been my boss. I nodded an affirmative response to his question, but I still couldn't remember saying such a thing.

"You know, my favorite story of his was *The Prince and the Pauper*; you know that one don't you?"

Again, I nodded. Keep in mind, when you play the family trump card, you'd better be familiar with every card in the deck and indeed I was.

"To wake up one day and be royalty; I wonder what that would be like."

"I don't know."

"Imagine waking up one day and you've gone from being a good stallion, to being a foundation stallion in establishing the greatest breed on the planet. Can you imagine going from a stud barn in one part of the world and the next day you're in the royal court of the queen. It's kind of like the story of the prince and the pauper, except in this case the prince and the pauper are one and the same. They don't change identities. They don't have to go back to being the pauper. No,

no, no – these three stallions are legends and each spent the rest of their lives in their new homes. They didn't live like princes. They lived like kings."

I was speechless. I knew nothing about race horses and know he was talking about Arabs and Kings all in one breath, as if I had any idea what he was talking about. I just nodded for the third time.

"What's the matter, Twain, cat got your tongue?"

He did it again; he called me Twain.

"No, I was . . . just"

"Just being polite, while I told the rest of the story. That's mighty nice of ya." Leonard took a sip of his water and started the long version of his story. "The first stallion was a war prize. A British Captain named Byerley brought back a black stallion from the conquered Turks. He took him from the area that's now Hungary and brought him back to England. To this day the horse is known as the Byerly Turk. He was bred to a few mares that started one line of the thoroughbred. Byerley spelt his name B Y E R L EY, but someone lost his E on the official records and now the stallion line is referred to by the spelling B Y E R L Y." Leonard's attention to such details was further testament to the extent of his knowledge.

"OK, so there's another E in Bylerly. I'm sure there has to be more to this stallion than how his name is spelled." I may have been getting a little grumpy waiting for my food.

"Try this. This almost black bay was a war horse when Captain Byerley claimed him as his personal victory prize at the Siege of Buda. The outcome of this battle changed the thoroughbred breed and horse racing forever. The stallion arrived in England around 1685, making him the first of the Three Kings to be imported."

"Three Kings?"

"That's right. What else would you call the three foundation stallions of the Sport of Kings?" Leonard said as his sandwich was set in front of him. He bowed his head, I assume he said a silent prayer. I eagerly grabbed my food; no more Mr. Grumpy. "Now, here's what really makes the Byerly Turk so rare. After being used at stud, Captain Byerley took the stallion back into battle action when the captain was sent to Ireland for King William's War and the Battle of Boyne in 1690. Funny enough, the Byerly Turk wasn't the only Turkish horse used in the Battle of Boyne.

The Dream Race

Another horse taken back to Ireland after the Siege of Buda became known as the Lister Turk. Imagine these two Turks encountering each other on the battlefield of Boyne as rivals after having been stable mates for Turkish officers."

"It's a small world." I said as I dug deeper into my sandwich.

"You got that right. It's amazing how these three kings came from all over the world and all ended up in various estates in the little country of England."

"They didn't end up at the same place?"

"No, not only that, but they all lived at different times. Uh huh, the second stallion was brought back to England almost twenty years after the Byerly Turk, around the 1700's."

"So, about three hundred years ago," I said.

"The food must be helping clear your mind."

"I was so hungry I could have eaten a . . . a soy burger." My choice of words had Leonard smiling. "OK, so tell me about the next foundation stallion."

"A gentleman named Thomas Darley imported this horse from what is now Syria. This stallion came from the desert and had lived in the tent with his Bedouin owners. One story says that Thomas Darley made a deal to buy the colt as a yearling from a sheik, but the sheik later reneged on the deal saying he couldn't part with such a wonderful colt. There is nothing more valuable to the Bedouins than great horses and it's obvious, this colt was one of a kind. The story goes on to say Darley paid some sailors to smuggle the horse out of the country any way they could. No one knows what really took place; but three years after the deal was originally struck the horse historians dubbed the Darley Arabian was in England.

"So, maybe Mr. Darley wasn't such a gentleman." I couldn't help putting my two cents in.

"Come to think of it, depending upon your point of perspective, Mr. Darley could be seen as a scoundrel; I'm sure at least one Arab sheik thought so. History is funny that way."

"Or not so funny depending upon your point of perspective." My reply got a grin out of Leonard.

"Well, this gentleman scoundrel, Darley, had an eye for horses and the Darley Arabian is found in more pedigrees today than the other two foundations stallions combined."

"Why do you think that is?" I asked.

"It might have been his size. He was a long, lean, and lanky bay; making him a quite bit taller than most Arabians. He was over fifteen hands that more than a hand taller than most Arabians of that era. It made him almost as tall as today's thoroughbreds. There are no photos of these horses and very few paintings made from them. So, we don't know for sure what they looked like, but all accounts have the Darley Arabian had extremely long slender legs with a blaze the length of his head. His height could have played a role in his progeny's success." Leonard tried his best to tell the story and eat. I was finished and was eyeing the second half of Leonard's sandwich.

"Are you going to eat that?"

"You're a growing boy, have at it. I'm not boring you, am I?"

"No, no; the Byerly Turk, the Darley Arabian, and . . . see I was listening."

"Listening and eating." Leonard countered as he handed me the rest of his sandwich.

"And . . ."

"And the last of the three kings is the Godolphin Barb."

"OK, I have to ask; why is one a Turk, one an Arabian, and one a Barb?" I forced the words out between bites.

"Good question. They're all desert horses. Some people say they are all the same breed, but there has to be some difference or people wouldn't have used three different terms all these years. The best answer I can give you is geography. It seems the Turks come from the upper regions of Persia, the Arabians originated out of the Middle East, while the Barbs come from North Africa."

"Isn't Egypt part of North Africa?"

"Exactly and that's why the terms are confused and interchanged. So, for all practical purposes the three kings are all called Arabians." Leonard's explanation made sense.

"So, this last horse, the Barb, is from Africa?"

"Actually, the Godolphin was imported from France."

"Alright, I'm ready. There has to be a lot more to this story. Bring it on."

"Good. Getting to England for the Godolphin Arabian is quite a story. As a matter of fact it actually is a book. Did you ever read any horse books when you were a kid?"

"I feel almost silly admitting it, but I did."

"Did you ever read *King of the Wind?*"

"Leonard, that sounds really familiar."

"It's one of those books that almost every child reads sometime in their life. Well, the story is the true story of the Godolphin Arabian. I imagine there's some creative doctoring going on with the story, but the travels of the stallion from the desert to Spain and on to France is true. According to the book, he even spent some time pulling a cart through the streets of Paris. This horse had one friend that went wherever he did; a tabby cat named Grimalkin."

"How'd he go from pulling a cart to being one of the three kings?"

"Read the book. It's a fun story, but the stallion passed to the Earl of Goldophin about twenty-five years after the Darley Arabian started producing foals in England. The three foundation stallions lived over a period of almost seventy five years and there's no proof that any of them ever met, but crosses of their get made the breed what it is."

"Crosses of their get . . . what does that mean?" I asked.

"Their get means their babies. Crosses of their get means breeding babies from one of the Arabian stallions with babies from the other Arabian stallions," Leonard answered.

"How do they know that? That's a pretty bold statement."

"A good reporter asks good questions and that, young man, was a good question. The first general stud book was released in 1790 by James Weatherby; that's a hundred years after the Byerly Turk was brought to England."

"Who keeps the official record?"

"It's The Jockey Club. Forty years before the first stud book was published the Jockey Club set up the first set of rules for racing."

"Who does it now?"

"Well, in England, it's the same people who have done it since day one. The Jockey Club still holds Weatherby's original stud book that listed 387 horses. No one ever realized the amazing fact that each of these thoroughbreds could be traced back to at least one of these three Arabians until Weatherby's publication came out. You see, King Charles II brought

horses to England from Spain as part of his dowry. His wife was the daughter of the King of Portugal. The mares he imported produced the base for what became the royal mares. These mares were later crossed with middle-eastern stallions. And you guessed it, the rest is history."

"Leonard, that's a pretty abrupt end to just say the rest is history. Would you mind elaborating?"

"Son, I thought you'd never ask. Let's take it from the present and go backwards. You ever seen those family tree charts people draw that show your mother and father, then it shows their mothers and fathers, and it keeps going back until you have this great big chart with dozens, maybe hundreds of people depending on how far back you go."

"Sure, the family tree stuff."

"Yeah, I'm sure there is a more scientific name than that, but at least we're on the same page. OK, so imagine going far enough back until you find out you're related to Adam."

"OK, hypothetically I'm with you."

"Well, sooner or later everybody is going to start having the same uncles, aunts, and grand-folks; if you could go back far enough."

"All right, I'm playing along with you."

"Well, on the pedigrees of any thoroughbred today, you'll start to see the same horses over and over. The farther back you go you start to see names like Native Dancer, Bold Ruler by Nasrullah, and Hyperion from the twentieth century; Persimmon, St. Simon, Domino, and Commando from the nineteenth century; and a handful of horses from the 1700's like King Herod, Flying Childers, Matchem, and Eclipse."

"Leonard, you know that right off the top of your head?"

"That's just some of the Darley Arabians line; you want to hear the Byerly or the Godolphin line next?"

"OK, ok, you made a believer out of me."

"You see, those charts keep getting wider and wider as they go farther back, but eventually those thoroughbred pedigrees start to narrow until they stop dead in their tracks, with unknown pedigrees lost forever in the deserts of Africa and the Middle East. Every thoroughbred pedigree chart either begins or ends with the Three Kings. It's just a matter of how you look at 'em."

"So, these charts go all the way back past the American Revolution." I noted.

"Boy, long before there was a president over here, there were thoroughbreds competing over there in 'The Sport of Kings'. Make no mistake, thoroughbred racing really did begin with kings and queens. As a matter of fact, it was a queen who played a large role in bringing order to the sport."

"Which Queen?"

"Queen Anne." Leonard said as he reached over and took the last bite of my sandwich out of my hands and ate it. OK, so I took it from him. At least, I asked.

"Who's Queen Anne?"

"She is credited with having the first course laid out specifically for racing horses. That's why the Three Kings Dream Race is going to take place on the grounds of her palace. Can you name a better place for these kings to run than a real palace; a palace that belonged to the queen who established the first race course?"

"I can't argue with that." I said as I grabbed the check from the waitress before she could even set it on the table.

"Twain, try to imagine tracing your family tree back that far. I mean it's one thing to go back to Sam Clemens, but it's quite another to go all the way back to the very beginning. I mean it would be like . . . be like . . ."

"Having a family tree going all the way back to Adam and Eve."

"Yeah, that would be about right; Adam and Eve. I guess you can't go back any farther than the book of Genesis; and kinda the same with the Byerly Turk, the Darley Arabian, and the Godolphin Arabian. They are to the thoroughbred, what Adam and Eve are to the Bible."

"Except, one is religion and the other is sport." I said.

"Boy, in these parts, you might learn that there ain't much difference."

"You mean, horse racing is like a religion to some people."

"Yeah, that too; but I was thinking in terms of faith. There's no such thing as a sure thing. Religion and horses both take a leap of faith. People can get rather worked up about both," Leonard said.

"I could see people praying at the races, but church is no place for crossing fingers."

"True, true. It isn't anything new, it's been that way since Queen Anne hosted the first race. As long as people race horses and make a friendly wager, it's gonna be that way."

"So, tell me more."

"Well, the governing body of the thoroughbred industry was set up in 1750, forty years before the first registry. The group still exists today."

"Were you there?"

"My, my, my . . . aren't we feelin' a little froggy today."

"Well, you seem to have known every horse that ever lived. I assumed you must have seen the three foundation stallions as well."

"You do know why you are never supposed to assume, don't you?"

"Not really." I replied, setting the bait for Leonard.

"'Cause, boy, it makes a donkey out of u and me," he said as he dissected the word on his napkin.

"What?"

"Think about it; let me know when you get it."

"Oh, ok I see it . . . the joke's on me."

"That's right, better on you than me. By the way I only saw two of the three kings." Leonard smiled and winked. "I never saw the Byerly Turk. I'm not that old."

and Eve."

"Well, you seem to have known every horse that ever lived. I assumed you must have seen the three foundation stallions as well."

"You do know why you are never supposed to assume, don't you?"

"Not really." I replied, setting the bait for Leonard.

"'Cause, boy, it makes a donkey out of u and me." He said as he dissected the word on his napkin.

"What?"

"Think about it; let me know when you get it."

"Oh, ok I see it . . . the jokes on me."

"That's right, better on you than me. By the way I only saw two of the three kings." Leonard smiled and winked. "I never saw the Byerly Turk. I'm not that old."

The Dream Race

Eclipse First: Late in the 18th Century England, Eclipse was undefeated in all of his races. He so over matched the competition that a catch phrase of his time became, "Eclipse First, and the rest nowhere"; which meant the horses were often out of sight when Eclipse crossed the finish line.

Eclipse First

We started our drive back to the barn after lunch in Leonard's old truck. His stories were filling my head with more information than I could possibly keep track of. There were the fillies, iron horses, near misses, and underdogs. He

Eclipse

told stories from great racing venues from all across the country and around the world. Leonard was an unending source of history, which he shared through his folksy form of backyard Iliad. The Dream Race was an epic tale with his stories of heartbreak and colossal accomplishments. Leonard's a living and breathing Ulysses who just happened to cruise around in a twenty-year-old rusting boat of a pick-up truck.

"Religion and horse racing." Leonard said with his eyes fixed to the horizon. He kept his hands steady as if at the helm of an ancient sailing ship. "Yeah, religion and horse racing; couldn't be more different and couldn't be more the same."

"What do you mean?" I knew Leonard had a reason for throwing out such a wild analogy out of the blue like that.

"Both will make you pray, a lot more than you would normally." He answered.

"Gimme that old time religion and the number six horse in the third race." I replied full of insincere gusto.

"I like that. Can I quote you? I'd love to get that on a bumper sticker."

Was Leonard serious? I had no idea.

"Bumper sticker, huh?"

"We could make millions or lose millions in the process. I guess that makes it kind of like the horse business." Leonard paused as he seemed to be contemplating one of nature's great mysteries. "I wonder how you say bumper sticker in Latin."

The Dream Race

"Chariot graffiti?" I answered.

"Gotta admit, it has a Latin ring to it."

"Seriously, Leonard, what's this obsession with Latin, religion and philosophy."

Leonard laughed, then turned and looked at me. He looked at me long enough that I was really beginning to wish he would look back at the road as the trees zoomed past us at fifty miles an hour.

"Boy, you don't think an old stable hand can be an educated man?"

"Well, . . . no . . . I . . .that's not wha . . ."

"Son, I'm gonna have to believe your hesitation more than your words. I think I know your real answer."

"No, it's not that I don't think you could . . . or someone could . . ."

"Don't sweat it, boy. I got something to show you."

About that time we passed the turn we should have taken to go back to the barn. I realized I may have hurt Leonard's feelings. Where he was taking me now was anyone's guess. I just hope it wasn't to a remote portion of the woods; I really didn't want to get my fanny whooped by a dual centurion; hardly a hundred pounds and nearly a hundred years old.

We pulled up to a nice house with a neatly kept yard. It looked more like a postcard than some place where someone actually lived. Leonard cut the engine.

"Come on, let's go inside. We've got a couple minutes."

I followed him to the cute door, complete with a welcome sign made out of horse shoes.

"Thelma, I'm home and I brought a guest with me."

"This is your house?" I'd already figured that out, but I asked anyhow. It might have been a stupid question, the kind reporters take a life time to overcome and would be better off if they (we) just kept our mouths shut; but then we wouldn't be who we are.

"No, I just walk into other people's houses all the time." OK, so it was definitely a stupid question; the name on the mailbox or the one on the door could have saved me the embarrassment.

A woman appeared from another room. She was wiping her wet hands on her apron. "It's always a pleasant surprise when my boyfriend drops by for a little afternoon delight."

"Boyfriend?" I whispered.

"Oh, don't worry young man. Leonard and I are married; have been for more years than either one of us care to discuss."

"Wait a minute, you're Thelma?"

"Always have been." She answered with the only smile I've ever seen that was wider than the one Leonard sported most of the time. I looked at Leonard.

"Thelma, the first kiss?" I whispered in his ear.

"Yep, and it's seventy-plus years of marriage and add a few more to get all the way back to that first kiss." Leonard announced as he leaned forward and kissed her on the cheek. She brushed him away with her apron playfully.

"Leonard, if you wanted to play house, you shouldn't have brought home company. Plus, you haven't even introduced the young man," she said with a pinch of his chin.

"Thelma, this is Allen Clemens. He's a reporter and he's doing a story on the greatest horse of all-time. Allen this is my bride, the beautiful Thelma."

I couldn't believe how cute the two of them were. It was a side of Leonard I hadn't seen before, but it didn't surprise me that he was as warm in his home life as he was with everyone else we had encountered during the day. They all loved him and none loved him more than this woman.

"Let me guess, you're telling Mr. Clemens all about the Dream Race."

"Yes ma'am, he is and I'm enjoying every minute of it." I answered for Leonard.

"Don't let the old coot fool you, he's having the time of his life telling you about it." She turned her attention from me to Leonard. "Well, as much as I'd like to believe you brought him here to meet me; go ahead show him your room." She turned her attention back to me. "I've been to a lot of museums that don't have half of what you're about to see. Now, go on, you

The Dream Race

boys go play; I've got work to do, unlike some folks around here."

Her playful spunk was the mirror of the way Leonard had throttled me all morning. I wondered who had it first and who learned it from whom; I guess it was a developed style that after nearly seventy years there wasn't an answer, just a lot of tongue-in-cheek companionship. Thelma popped Leonard on the tail with her apron and chased us out of the room.

We went into an adjacent room. Even as a person whose profession is built upon words, I still have a hard time describing it. The room was part library, part art gallery, it was a museum, it was a scrapbook with walls. The room was a time capsule that had never been sealed; the time capsule was always open, but only those Leonard deemed worthy ever saw it. The collection was a journey back in time; through pictures, framed letters, and paintings. There were postcards tacked to a large board. The board was buried under three or four layers of notes and snapshots. There were shelves filled with trophies, plaques, and ribbons. Bookcases filled any space not covered with pictures. Leonard had hundreds, maybe thousands of books. Every crack between the book cases was stuffed with magazines. The room looked as if Einstein, Edison, Socrates,

Descartes, and daVinci shared the space. There were many books on horses, but the vast majority were on a wide array of topics. Something peculiar was the dust; or better said, the lack of it. There was not any dust, no cob webs, and no clutter. Leonard had everything neatly organized, which may have been the one difference between Leonard's museum and the workshops of some of history's legendary minds. Other than that, this was a goldmine of intellectual richness. It was also a treasure of thoroughbred memorabilia, most of which was personally addressed to Leonard.

"Incredible" was the only word that came out of my mouth as I turned slowly in an attempt to take it all in. Each time I looked up, down, or around some other trinket would catch my eye. Also, I couldn't get a real sense of the size of the room. I couldn't tell if it was a large room shrunk with wall to wall mementos or if it was a small room bursting at the seams. Either way, Leonard's wife was right; this collection was more substantial than most small museums. Plus, it was personalized. It truly was Leonard's museum,

Leonard's library; it was Leonard's whatever you want to call it. I still don't have the right words to describe it, but it was impressive and it was his.

I made my way over to one of the bookcases. I may not have been an expert on the history of the thoroughbred; but I did know a little something about literature. What I saw amazed me. He had all the classics, from contemporary literature back to the earliest recorded writing. He had a lot of obscure works, which I had never heard of. He had books by authors I had read, books by authors I had only heard of. Then the realization hit me like a ton of bricks; Leonard was better read than I was. I had made certain assumptions based upon his job, the way he dressed, and the way he spoke. I guess I even made the same assumptions regarding his general intelligence.

"Leonard, you read all of these?"

"Most of most of 'em, at least some of all of 'em, and all of a few of 'em. Socrates can only be read in small bits with a lot of chewing."

I picked up one of the books with Socrates on the hand written label. When I flipped it open, the book was written in Latin.

"Leonard, did you read this one?"

He looked at the cover.

"Yeah, that was one of the better ones."

"It's in Latin."

"Boy, you know the old saying, 'It gets lost in the translation.' Well, it's the truth. You can read what someone said he said; or you can read it for yourself. Nothin' quite like getting it straight from the horse's mouth."

"You read Latin fluently? Nobody reads Latin."

"I guess I'm just nobody." He laughed, "truth be known, I don't read it fluently; I can just get by. I guess, if I ever get lost in Latin, I'll be able to ask for directions. That's about it." Leonard could afford to be humble. He knew he had me. If you thought speaking Latin was difficult, you should try English sometime with a mouthful of crow, a slice of humble pie, and one of your own feet.

The Dream Race

"Leonard, how . . . I mean why . . . I mean . . ."

"What possessed me to read all this stuff?"

"Well, yeah"

"That little lady in the other room, number one. She was a school teacher for almost forty years. The whole time she was going to college to be a teacher; I was working on horse farms. Doing whatever I could to pay the bills. One day I was waiting to pick her up at school and I find myself sitting in the library. I picked up a book just to pass the time and the next thing you know, I was reading everything I could get my hands on. I still do and I'm really looking forward to your article on the Dream Race."

Here was a man who could break down all my prejudices and preconceived ideas with nothing more than a smile and a wink. He never had to raise his voice and didn't need my approval. There was one thing I understood, now more than ever before; never judge a book by its cover. Leonard was such a book and this old book was becoming better with each enticing page, each chapter, and every story. Leonard was the perfect person to tell the fascinating story of the Dream Race. Any further proof to substantiate this fact was right in front of me in all the pictures of Leonard with hundreds of different horses, jockeys, trainers, and owners.

"This is . . . this is . . ."

"Interesting?" Leonard tried to fill in the blank for me.

"No, well, yes it is that, but it's something else. It's . . .it's . . ."

"Unusual?"

"No, that's not the word I'm looking for . . .it's . . .it's . . . perfect. That's it; it's perfect!" At last, I found the perfect description. "Perfect!"

"I'll take that as a compliment, but it's not perfect. Nothing is perfect . . .well, nothing except a few special horses and maybe one horse that was just a little more perfect than the rest." With that said, Leonard walked over to a specific photo on the wall. "This one was perfect." Then he pointed at another photo of him with another horse. "So, was this one. Perfect is as rare in horse racing as it is anywhere else; but perfection is possible. Oh, yes, my young friend,

perfection is possible; 'cause I have seen it with my own eyes and touched it with these hands."

"Who are those horses?"

"That one is Ribot, he ran over in Europe and retired undefeated. This big bay filly is Personal Ensign, remember her from the Dream Distaff? Their stories are far more interesting than my little trophy room."

"I don't know about that, this place is pretty interesting." I said. Then, I studied the two horse photos Leonard pointed out, but I couldn't help looking around at the hundreds of pictures in the room. Out of all these horses and all the ones Leonard had told me about already; these were the only two that he singled out as being perfect. The greatest of the best, the best of the greatest; this had to be the answer to my quest. Leonard had made his point by showing me this room and now he was going to give me the answer to my question. One of these 'perfect' horses had to be the greatest of all-time; after all you can't get better than perfect, can you?

I looked at the wall nearest to me. The first picture to catch my eye was one with a small black child holding the lead line on a big horse along side an old white man who was bent over to the point of being deformed. I realized it was Leonard. The photo had to be at least seventy years old.

I looked back at Leonard and noticed he was reading the personal message on one of the photos. He read it as if it was the first time he had ever seen it. He acted like a guest in his own museum.

"Leonard, that's it, only two undefeated horses out of the thousands upon thousands who have raced; are there only two perfect horses?"

"Let's get a couple things straight. First, the two perfect horses were perfect on the track. Secondly, there were other undefeated horses. These two happen to be the ones I have known. Nearly a century ago there was another colt who retired with an unblemished record. His name was Colin and was undefeated over two racing seasons, fifteen races. His first win was in a field of twenty-two horses, and Colin even beat a strong race horse named Fair Play a couple of times. Oh, you may know Fair Play better as Man o' War's sire. The meteoric career of Colin was a flash of brilliance, which endures in thoughts of what could have been. By today's standards his career may not be considered that short; but in his era the best horses might have forty or more starts to their credit. Oh, yeah being retired at three was regretfully too short. Especially when you consider his potential was never fully tapped."

"Why was he retired so young?"

"He had been hurt several times, but kept racing and winning. The last time was just too much to overcome and the undefeated colt had run his last race."

"That's too bad."

"Yeah, Colin was a hard luck horse from the get go. He came from a line of sires with just as bad luck. His grandsire was a horse named Domino. Now, that horse is still remembered today as a great stallion, yet he only produced twenty foals before he died. His most famous son was Commando who only produced twenty-seven foals. When you think about it, the whole Domino line could have disappeared by now; instead it is still one of the strongest blood lines today despite the small number of foals. Colin was just like 'em, real fast and just cursed with bad luck on and off the track."

"What happened off the track?"

"Son, everybody knows about the Great Depression, but did you know that after the turn of the last century America went into one of its worst depressions?"

"No, I guess I didn't."

"Well, some bright politicians got together in Washington and figured the depression somehow resulted from horse racing. Well, you know their solution to everything." Leonard let me answer.

"Change the law and make it illegal?"

"No, they didn't make horse racing illegal . . . worse, they made betting on horses illegal. Son, gambling is like mother's milk to racing. They made betting illegal in 1908 just after Colin set the juvenile standard with a perfect twelve for twelve. His three-year old campaign came under the new no gambling law."

"And that was when Colin stopped racing," I commented.

"No he still ran in a couple races with no gambling, but the crowds were a mere fraction of what

they had been."

"Leonard, I don't get it then."

"Racing was still legal in the UK. So, Colin was shipped to England to race over there. Before he could run his first race in England, he blew out his legs again and this time it was too serious to let him run again. Colin never got to show off for the English or their book makers. A year or so later, gambling was legal again at the U.S. tracks. By then, Colin had retired with an untarnished record. Whether he remained undefeated or not, his short career hurts his claim to greatness. The horse industry bestows greatness on its very best stars; not its shooting stars."

He steered me to an old picture. "That was Colin. He could have been the twentieth century's first superstar. He could have been much more than a shooting star. Yes sir, this is one horse I wish I could have seen in person."

"Is Colin in the Dream Race?" I asked.

"Yeah, he's there in one of the smallest fields of the Dream Race, but it's a special group. His race is simply called 'Perfection'."

"So, who would you say would win the 'Perfection Race'? It sounds to me as if you think it would be between Ribot and Colin, right?"

Leonard took a moment to review the pictures on his wall. He's looked at them so many times, they were merely snapshots of the Dream Race in his imagination. Leonard paused before answering.

"Did you notice the really old poster? It was . . ."

"Funny looking?" I said filling in the blank even before it was a blank.

Leonard laughed. "Yeah, it seems every artist from that time period painted horses the same way. They'd always be flying through the air with their legs spread as wide apart as possible. No matter how many horses were in the paintings; all of them had their legs stretched out like they were made of rubber and then cast in steel."

"Yeah, and they look like cartoons too." I was on a roll. I guess you don't have to be expert to be a critic; or even know what you're talking about for that matter.

"I think the accepted term the art historians prefer to use is stylized." Leonard corrected me and then added with a wink, "Critics just can't seem to say cartoon, no matter what."

Leonard waited for me to wipe the smile off my face. "The horse is Eclipse and if he's in the race with the other perfect horses, I'm afraid there would be a few less perfect horses left when the race was over."

"Eclipse, uh. Was he that good?"

"Well, as you are starting to learn there are horses that were good on the track and horses that were good producers of race horses."

"And which was Eclipse?"

"Well, if you'd asked me that question about two hundred years ago, my answer would have been the track. Now, I'd have to say the only thing greater than Eclipse on the track has been his long term impact on the breed."

"He was a great stallion?" I asked.

"Well, some of his babies were good, real good; but here's the real number you should remember: 95."

"What's 95?"

"That is the percent of thoroughbreds alive today estimated to be a descendant of Eclipse." Leonard answered.

"Wow, seriously?"

"Seriously, the truth may only be 80%, but either way when you are talking about tens of thousands of horses the numbers are mind boggling."

"All right, you got my attention. Tell me more about this incredible horse."

"Incredible is not an understatement. The highest award handed out every year is the Eclipse Award. I can't think of a higher tribute to any horse. The award has kept the legend alive, by keeping the name in front of the public. Keep in mind, we're talking about a horse that was born before America declared its independence from England. He was actually born in 1764 during a major solar eclipse, hence he was named after the phenomenon. Quite fitting, seeing the type of phenomenon he created when he went to the track was something out of this world."

"Perfection, right?"

"Perfection and then some. This is a horse that ran eighteen times."

"And won every time." I had a way of jumping in a little prematurely. Leonard had a way of making me wish I hadn't.

"Not only did he win every time, he won big. When a horse wins by over 240 yards, it called distance. Eclipse not only won, he distanced 'em; not just a few horses, but in most races the entire field was distanced. Eclipse's legend was put to words at the track when Captain O'Kelly put his money where his mouth was. He announced his bet out loud, 'Eclipse first, and the rest no where.' That was another way of saying Eclipse would distance the entire field and of course, he did. Boy, did you ever play a game of horse in basketball?"

"Oh, yeah, but . . ."

"So, you understand what is meant by 'calling your shot'?" Leonard asked.

"Yes."

"Well, I'd have to say Captain O'Kelly was the first to call his shot in a game of horse . . . and he did it a hundred years before the game of basketball was invented."

"So, Eclipse wins the 'Perfection' Dream Race."

"He'd have to."

"And where does this race take place?"

"Young man, that's a good question and shows you've figured out the concept of the Dream Race. To answer your question, take a look at this." Leonard pointed at a print filled with horses and jockeys. It was somewhat faded, but despite that, the print was brightly colored. The horses weren't realistic, but they seemed more real in some ways. They had lifelike action and the crowds of people around them seemed to be moving like a dark swarm of bees with little bands of color. "Do you recognize it?"

I wasn't an art major. I merely met my college requirement for art appreciation. I shook my head. No.

"Degas"

The Dream Race

"I thought he painted ballet dancers?" OK, so I didn't sleep through every art appreciation class.

"True, he is famous for his ballet dancers, but the facts are, Degas painted horses the way the human eye sees them and not how the brain remembers them." Leonard looked back at the old picture from the 1700's with all the horses' legs being stretched to their breaking point. "This is the way artists saw them in their minds. The problem was they couldn't get a horse to pose in mid stride and this is how horses were painted by almost every artist of this era." Leonard looked back at the Degas print. "Degas didn't need them to pose. He just painted what he saw. His paintings were more like snapshots, a split second of time brought to life on his canvas. Look at the crowd; they're people, but he isn't painting every little eye ball or even every little face. He lets our brain fill in those details." Leonard paused before repeating my question. "So, where does Eclipse run his Dream Race?"

I must have nodded to confirm the question.

"Well, let me tell you how I see it." Leonard said. "Or better yet, let me tell you how Degas might have seen it. Eclipse ran a few years before the American Revolution; Degas lived more than a hundred years later. During Eclipse's lifetime gentlemen were still wearing their white wigs and stretched stockings instead of full length pants. The Epsom Derby ran for the first time in 1780. Unfortunately, maybe the greatest horse England has ever seen never raced in the Epsom Derby. I think the Perfection Dream Race would be the perfect opportunity for Eclipse to race for a crowd of Englishmen a hundred years later at a time when the top hat was the style, when the men wore derbies to the Derby. The women would be in their flowing brightly colored dresses and matching parasols accenting the black, charcoal grey, and brown suits worn by the gentlemen. Of course, the outcome would still be the same. There just wouldn't be any photographs of the race; only the images from an artist like Degas. In England it's usually pretty cold during the Derby, but imagine a bright sunny day. The men are in their black suits and top hats. All the ladies' parasols sprinkled across the landscape like the place where rainbows touch the earth."

"Eclipse first, and the rest no where." I repeated.

"Yep, that's right. No disrespect to Colin, Ribot, Nearco, or even Personal Ensign; but this is Eclipse's race and that's all there is to it."

Leonard walked out of the room leaving me alone with all of his treasured memories. I knew it was time to go, but I took another look at the painting of Eclipse; then, another scan of everything. I remembered the one word to describe Leonard's prized room; one simple word, 'perfect'.

Men of War: Three generations of Man o' War: In 1917 August Belmont II enlisted into the army at the age of 65. The last horse he sold was a yearling later known as Man o' War. Two of Man o' War's most successful descendents were his son, the Triple Crown winner, War Admiral and his grandson, the legendary Seabiscuit.

Men of War

"Three generations of greatness." That was the way Leonard started off a lot of his thoughts. They weren't complete sentences; it was more like the pieces of coming attractions they play at the movie theater, just a little something to whet the appetite.

"Three generations of greatness." I repeated. Repeating had become my way of getting Leonard to go into greater detail. The casual listener would have thought I had a

Men of War

1. Man o' War
2. War Admiral
3. Seabiscuit

hearing problem, but Leonard knew what I wanted a ticket to the coming attraction, the next fantasy race.

"Yeah, there's been many a horse that's produced good babies, but when you talk about horses who were great on the track and just as great in the stud barn; that's when the legend of Man o' War grows even more."

"Man o' War?" See, I repeated him again. That means I'll be getting a good sized serving of this story with all the sweet trimmings.

"Yeah, one of my best memories was being able to see Big Red. Man o' War's groom, Will Harbut, called him 'the mostest horse'. I was just a kid and everything seemed so much bigger. The mind has a funny way of making things from the past even larger than they really were. So, in my memory I see a horse that's larger than life, a real giant; but then again – he was. Yes sir, that was the horse, maybe the greatest horse of all-time and when he went to the breeding shed; more often than not, he was liable to knock out a winner. No horse could compare to his greatness, except maybe one he produced. During the Roaring 20s the horse track was the place to be and Man o' War was the king. For even a close comparison you had to look at someone like Babe Ruth. The whole world talked about the Babe being the best athlete on two legs, but when people talked about the best athlete, period; the conversation usually came down to none other than Man o' War. He only lost once; ironically to a horse named Upset. To this day many people think the term 'upset' is used for a long shot who beats the odds came from that race. It makes for a better story than truth. It adds to his legacy to think words in the dictionary were created just to describe his unique talent. In 1947 Will Harbut died of a heart attack and less than a month later Man o' War died as well. I think it was loneliness. Those two were inseparable and you can bet that Will is gonna be the man putting the saddle on Man o' War for the Dream Race. Yeah, Man o' War, now, that was a horse; maybe, just maybe 'the mostest horse' of 'em all."

"Next you're going to tell me they even had a funeral for 'the mostest horse'."

"Sure did, thousands came to the funeral. Man o' War was on public display in his giant coffin; but that ain't the half of it, millions of people around the country listened to the memorial service over the radio."

"You're kidding, right? I mean, Leonard, you can't be serious; on the radio."

"I'll avoid the silly puns as to how serious I am. Trust me, boy, it happened just like I said it did."

"Can't argue with 'the mostest', I guess that is as good as it gets." Sometimes I have to be careful not to sound smug. I was sincere, but I even sounded less than that to myself.

"One important thing to remember when talking about Man o' War is the man behind the name. Man o' War was bred by August Belmont II."

"Belmont, as in . . . ?"

"Yep, those Belmonts; his grandfather built Belmont Park. The family had been in racing for generations. Then the 'War to End All Wars' came along. You see, that's what they called it back then. Why would any one call it World War One, unless they knew they weren't going to get it right the first time."

"You've got a point there."

"Now, we've all heard stories of war heroes; but I'm gonna tell you about one who didn't fire a shot or even get shot at. That was August Belmont. That's right. When the United States entered the war in 1917, Mr. Belmont enlisted in the military. Now, that wasn't so unusual by itself; millions of

young men were signing up all across the country. The difference was that Mr. Belmont was sixty-five years old."

"Sixty-five?" This time when I repeated Leonard, I was truly shocked by what he'd said.

"Uh huh, sixty-five. He took over the role of training the horses for the U.S. Cavalry. Remember, horses had always been the key to military success since the days Genghis Khan rode all over Asia and perfected the science of a horseback warfare. Read Sun Tzu's *Art of War* from centuries ago, to see the importance of the horse in military conquests. Peter the Great wouldn't have been so great without the horse in his Russian empire. Napoleon led all of his campaigns from horseback and General George Washington was as great a horseman as there was in all the colonies. The same could be said of several officers during the Civil War. Good ole U.S. Grant was one of the best riders ever to come out of West Point. At the start of World War I, the horse was still the most important force on land. This didn't change until war became mechanized. So, Belmont's work with the horses was vital at that time and don't forget the other thing."

"What's the other thing?"

"Yeah, didn't I mention Belmont sold off all of his young horses?"

"No, Leonard, I guess you missed that small detail," as if Leonard ever missed a detail, large or small.

"Oh, well he did. He wasn't gonna have time to get to the track to train the new crop; so, he up and sold 'em all. The last one Belmont let go was his favorite, a blood red chestnut. After Sam Riddle bought the colt, he changed the name in honor of Belmont. Riddle named him Man o' War."

"You're kidding"

"No sir, unlike the story about Upset, sometimes the truth is too good of a story to embellish. This is one of those times."

"And Mr. Riddle was the one who raced him?"

"That's right. He put Man o' War on the track carrying his black and gold silks with six gold hoops around each sleeve. In 1919 he started his career on the track at two. Ironically, 1919 was the first time a three-year-old, Sir Barton, collected the Kentucky Derby, the Preakness, and the Belmont all in the same year. It was the first Triple Crown and no one even called it that yet."

The Dream Race

"Let me see if I've got this straight; during the '20s World War I wasn't called World War I and the Triple Crown wasn't called the Triple Crown."

"You got it. Keep in mind in 1919 these weren't the most prestigious races or the ones with the highest purses at the time. That's why Sir Barton's accomplishment would have amounted to an asterisk in a record book at the time, kind of like poor ole Roger Maris when he broke Babe Ruth's home run record."

"Asterisk?"

"I keep forgetting you're not old enough to drink or vote, much less know about your basic sports history."

"I'm old enough to vote in the next election."

"That's a comforting thought." I wasn't sure where Leonard's dry sense of humor ended and his real concerns began, but I pretended to laugh and tried not to look too embarrassed.

"Boy, the truth is Man o' War could have been the second Triple Crown winner in 1920, if Mr. Riddle thought it was worth winning at the time. To him the Kentucky Derby was just a race in Kentucky too early in the year to be safe for his prized three year old who had just beaten the world in his two year old season. Why risk injury when the prize didn't warrant takin' the chance?"

"The Triple Crown wasn't worth winning?"

"Wasn't worth winning, boy, it didn't even exist until some east coast writer scribbled the line in one of his newspaper columns. The term stuck and that was over ten years after Sir Barton won the first one and long after Man o' War had been retired to stud."

"OK, since we're talking about the Dream Race, who would have won between Sir Barton and Man o' War?"

"That's simple – Man o' War."

"I knew that was going to be your answer."

"I would even say that he would win by nearly twenty lengths."

"Twenty lengths? Isn't that a bit much?"

"Not if it really happened and it did. Sir Barton and Man o' War met in a match race in 1920. Just the two of them, alone on the track, and the winner by a blow out was Man o' War. Sir Barton would later take his place in history when he

become known as the first Triple Crown winner. Imagine the hype before the match race between Sir Barton and Man o' War; and never hearing the term Triple Crown winner to describe the four-year-old champ. The way Man o' War put him away made it clear who was the king of the track and all the fancy titles and media hype wasn't going to change a thing. Man o' War wore the only crown that mattered on that day."

If I had said anything it would've detracted from the magnitude of what Leonard was telling me.

"Son, you see he was almost perfect on the track and it's a rare horse that passes talent like that on to his get. Big Red did it as well as any horse before or since. You only have to look as far as the fourth Triple Crown winner, a horse named War Admiral. He was a big almost black stallion that towered over the field. He wore the same black and gold silks of Mr. Riddle with five hoops on the sleeves."

"I thought you said there were six hoops," I interrupted. Was this the chink in Leonard's suit or armor, a mistake on his facts?

"I wondered how closely you were listening."

"Not that it really matters, but which was it, five or six?" I asked thinking I'd caught Leonard's error.

"Oh, it does matter. You see Mr. Riddle must have been a sentimental man. He named Man o' War as a tribute to his breeder, Mr. Belmont. He also removed one of the gold hoops from the sleeves of his silks when Man o' War retired as a tribute to the champion. It really does matter."

"Yeah, I guess it does."

"War Admiral was the best of Man o' War's sons. This big almost black colt was a beast on the track. His size was intimidating and his speed dominating. When War Admiral won the Triple Crown in '37; he was called unbeatable. Ironically, his greatest race may have been the one he lost."

"A loss was his most famous race?"

"Yep, some say it was the greatest race ever."

"So, who beat the unbeatable horse?"

"A relative of sorts; it was a Man o' War grandson. He was a small plain little brown horse by a mean son of . . . Man o' War named Hard Tack, a term used for the stale bread fed to sailors. Another name for hard tack is a sea biscuit and it's Seabiscuit that beat War Admiral in a match race. Mr.

The Dream Race

Riddle's Man o' War was the big winner in the match race against Sir Barton. However, Mr. Riddle was reluctant to put his Triple Crown winner on the track against a horse with little to lose and everything to gain. It almost took an act of Congress to get the two horses on the track in a match race and when it finally did happen; forget about Congress, even President Franklin Delano Roosevelt stopped everything to listen to the race on the radio. FDR heard the race along with millions of Americans. The country was almost evenly divided into two camps. People from the west were for Seabiscuit and Easterners backed War Admiral. Seabiscuit took his jockey, George Woolf, to an easy win. Not a bad substitute, I might add. Woolf was the best. They called him the Ice Man 'cause he was so cool in the saddle. No one knew it, except a few of the jockeys, but Woolf had diabetes. When you are always dieting to make weight, being a jockey may not be the best profession, but the Ice Man did one thing better than any one else, win races. That's what he did right up until his last race; when he fell and was killed. Some say his diabetes made him pass out. I don't know about that, but the one thing I can say for sure is Woolf was as good as they came. To this day, each year the best jockey wins the George Woolf Memorial Award."

"Wow, this is really amazing. I have to admit, I was just writing an article to begin with, but now I really am interested. Thank you, Leonard, I really appreciate it."

"You're welcome, Twain. Didn't I hear that you're some distant relative to the writer?"

"I've been meaning to ask you about that. Who did you hear it from, my boss, Mr. Williams, right?"

"We've spoken from time to time." Leonard rushed through his answer. "There are a lot worse people a person could be related to. I for one, really like Mark Twain. I love the story about the Calaveras County frog jumping contest. I still bust a gut laughing every time I read the part where they feed the frogs buckshot to keep 'em from jumping. Man, now that's funny. I think Twain would have been a fun man to play cards with, even have a shot or two with, and definitely a hoot to go to the track with." While Leonard talked I began laughing. "What's so funny?" Leonard asked.

"Well, I just wondered if Mark Twain would take a page from the Calaveras County frog races."

"What do you mean?"

I couldn't answer the question without continuing to laugh. "I just got this picture in my head of Mark Twain with his white coat, brushy mustache, and a couple bowling balls trying to shove them down the horses' mouths to slow them down."

I could tell Leonard got the visual. His smirk was my reward. "You know, son, you have to be a Clemens to come up with that one."

"Coming from you, Leonard; I'll take that as a compliment."

" OK, so you're a little creative, but Mark Twain was as cutting as he was witty, maybe the original political humorist. Now, there was a man with a gift for words. If I could go back in time, he would have been the man I would have wanted to write the story of the Dream Race. He could have given it the kind of twists to make you laugh and the punch to make you cry. You know, young man, you're starting to show me the spirit of a writer. Maybe you have some of your uncle in you after all. I'd like to read how you tell the story of the Dream Race, but I'd like to ask one thing."

"Sure, what is it?"

"When you tell the story of three generations of Man o' War, would you place it at Belmont Park. I never met Mr. Belmont; but if could give up such a great horse to serve his country, then the least we could do is honor him by letting these three horses run on the track named for his family."

"It's a deal." Truth be known, I couldn't have agreed more; I wish it had been my idea.

"Belmont's infield has eleven monuments with the names and silks of the Triple Crown winners and in bold letters, BELMONT is spelled out. Right next to that name should be one more name, MAN O' WAR."

The Dream Race

After Affirmed: After Affirmed won the Triple Crown in 1978 there have been several horses who have won the first two jewels in the Triple Crown only to be stopped on their quest in the Belmont Stakes; some by a little as a nose, another by a stubble, some by long shots, and even one by a safety pin.

After Affirmed

Afternoon was full force. Jackets worn in the morning chill were long since discarded.

"Leonard, can I ask you a question?"

"It seems to me you just did," Leonard said as he pulled a piece of hay out of a bale and stuck it into his mouth

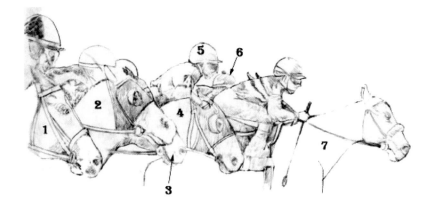

After Affirmed

1. Charismatic
2. Real Quiet
3. War Emblem
4. Alysheba
5. Sunday Silence
6. Pleasant Colony
7. Silver Charm

somewhere between his tongue and cheek, which seemed to be his most common form of reply – tongue in cheek.

"That's funny, so can I ask another?"

"Yeah, you just did again."

"OK, how about a couple of questions?"

"I don't know. What did you have in mind?"

"Well, everybody seems hung up on the Triple Crown, but the more we talk the more it seems there are a lot of good horses who never won the Triple Crown."

"Yeah, but that's not a question." He continued to chew the straw in his mouth while agilely avoiding the tongue in his cheek.

"Right, but after Affirmed have there been any great horses?"

"Well, now, I hope you noticed before you were talking about good horses and now you are talking about great horses. Do you mind if I ask you a question?" He said with a wink before I could turn the tables of semantic irony back on him. I nodded. "Which ones do you want to talk about?"

"Which ones? Which horses?"

"Nah, not which ones, but what kind; the good ones or the great ones?"

"Well, the great ones of course."

"Then, young man, I guess you had better define the difference, so as I don't waste your time talking about the wrong ones."

"The great ones, the ones everybody knows about; the famous ones . . ."

"Famous? Famous to who the people at the country club, office water cooler, or the people at the track? You see famous to one group may not be so famous to the other."

I knew Leonard had a point, but he wanted me to figure it out on my own, as opposed to handing it to me like a diamond already cut and polished.

"Boy, for example you came down here asking about who the greatest horse of all-time was. I mean real quick we can narrow that down to a small handful of horses and that handful would not be exclusive to only Triple Crown winners."

"Right . . ." Leonard was leading, but I was still unsure where it was I was supposed to be following him.

"Here's another question for you. Is Affirmed the best horse in the past thirty years?"

"Well, no one else has won the Triple Crown since he did it in . . . in . . ."

"'78"

"Yeah, '78. So, doesn't that make him the best?"

"Let's see how well you've been doing on your homework. Who did Affirmed beat in the three classics?"

"Alydar." My answer brought a smile to Leonard's face, which brought a smile to mine.

"Right, does that mean, if there wasn't an Affirmed that Alydar would have been the eleventh Triple Crown winner?"

"I don't know?"

"Boy, a lot of people think so. He came in second all three times to the same horse; if Affirmed wasn't there, would the question be whether Alydar was the best horse in the past twenty-five years?"

"Well, yeah if you put it that way, I guess he would be; but . . ." I knew there was something wrong with this logic, I just couldn't put it into words. Then I realized Leonard had led me to the exact point he was trying to make.

"Go on, son"

"But, you can't assume Alydar would have won all three races or for that matter, you can't assume that other horses over the past twenty-five years wouldn't have beaten Alydar or . . ."

"Or . . . go on" Leonard knew I was on the verge of suggesting the unthinkable and he wasn't going to let me pull up short of the finish line.

"Or for that matter, it might not be fair to assume that Affirmed would have beaten every horse over the past twenty-five years." I said.

"Now, you're thinking. Just don't say it too loud around the wrong people; you could be picking up your teeth off the floor or taken away by men in white coats."

I laughed while Leonard continued.

"Boy, the first thing you learn in the horse business is that races are won on the track, the second thing is that favorites have followings, and the third thing is that rivalries don't end at the finish line. Sometimes that is the place where they really get started."

The blank stare on my face must have begged for more information.

"So, you want an example. I'll give a couple examples right off the top of my head. Let's start with maybe the best rivalry since Affirmed and Alydar; that could be Sunday Silence and Easy Goer. Sunday Silence was a beautiful black colt bred by Arthur Hancock's Stone Farm. His family has been breeding winners for over a hundred years at Claiborne Farm. Sunday Silence wasn't even the favorite going into the Derby that was Easy Goer's title. By the time Belmont rolled around, the whole world was convinced that Sunday Silence was going to win the first Triple Crown since Affirmed. Everyone had forgotten about Easy Goer, but he had another idea. It was one of the greatest races I've ever seen. I was heartbroken as I cheered for the black colt. When it was over I cried, that's right, I cried when I realized what an incredible

91

race I had just seen. The same can be said of so many others after Affirmed. In '79 just one year after Affirmed, it wasn't such a big deal. There had been three crown winners in the previous six years, two in the last two years when you figure Seattle Slew the year before Affirmed. Spectacular Bid was supposed to make it three crowns in three years. That's why when Spectacular Bid came up one race short after being a huge favorite to win the Belmont; the story wasn't the near miss at another crown winner, as much as it was the rumors flying around about the safety pin found in the Bid's hoof the morning of the Belmont."

"You told me about that earlier and I'm still stunned," I said.

"Some people still play the game of 'who done it'; but time solves unsolved mysteries by fading them away. The amazing thing is that the big gray horse still competed like a champion and put on such a valiant effort. I think if the Bid had scratched that day at Belmont racing would still be hurting. I saw a gymnast at the Olympics a couple of years ago on TV. She sprained her ankle, but still did her last vault for the good of the team. It was one of the most heroic performances of all-

time. She knew she was hurt, but she wasn't going to give up. I think she might be one of the few humans who can really understand the heart of a horse like Spectacular Bid."

"Kerry Shrug."

"Yeah, that was her name. I thought you didn't know a lot about sports." Leonard said.

"I don't, but that was bigger than sports, that was . . . it was."

"Heroic?"

"Yeah, that's it."

"You see, son, heroic comes in many forms. It could be a little girl or a powerful horse, but they shared the kind of determination that never gives up."

"I can tell you really liked Spectacular Bid."

"Loved him." Leonard looked around the room as if to find something to clean, put away, or just something to do. Then, continued. "A couple years later it was Pleasant Colony with his great big whop-ears whistling down the backstretch. Oh yeah, he was ridden by Jorge Velazquez who had ridden

Alydar in the duel with Affirmed. He's seen his fair share of good horses and Pleasant Colony was as close as any to being immortalized with the crown. I still blame it on his ears, no horse could tote those big mule ears a mile and half. It was like the parachute on the back of a dragster; it was just too much to ask. If you say Affirmed won the crown by a nose, then Pleasant Colony lost it by an ear. Got to give the old boy his due though, he could really run and he's put out his fair share of winners."

Leonard took me around the side of the barn to show me something special. He knew this place like the back of his hand.

"See there," Leonard pointed to a stall with a big dark colt. "That's a grandson of Pleasant Colony and if my guess is right in about two years, if you're smart you'll be playin' his number."

The horse was too huge to be a yearling.

"He's a weanling?" I couldn't believe my eyes.

"Ahhuh, that's right." Leonard had a way of nodding his head like some old blues musician. The rhythm of his body language said more than words. He would just nod a couple times; the more I got to know him, the more it meant. It went from being a simple yes, to being a full dissertation. He was the silent orator. Without moving his lips, it was clear he was impressed with the big colt. It wasn't that he couldn't put it into words, he just didn't have to.

"Leonard, would you put Pleasant Colony in the Dream Race?"

"Like the Dream Distaff for the greatest fillies of all-time, I would have another race. I'd call this race the 'After Affirmed Stakes'."

"And that is where you would put Pleasant Colony?" I asked.

"Yeah, that's right."

"Who else would you have in the race with Spectacular Bid and Pleasant Colony?"

"The rest and a couple more." Leonard's vague answer was obviously deliberate.

"What rest and who's a couple more?"

93

The Dream Race

"I'd start with all the horses who went to the Belmont with a shot at the crown; those horses with the first two jewels in their purses only to come up short of gettin' it all."

Being a novice, I needed a little more information than that. "How many more of them are there?"

"Well, let's see. Sunday Silence would be there. Like I said, he was a horse I would have bet the farm on to win it all. He had it all, but Easy Goer was not havin' any part of being denied in all three classics. That was '89. In '87 Alysheba seemed unbeatable; until Bet Twice took the Belmont. Alysheba was an Alydar son and was so close to avenging history for his sire, but in the end his fate was also a near miss. He was trained by Jack Van Brunt. Mr. Van Brunt trained for almost fifty years. His father is also a Hall-of-Fame trainer and I guess between 'em they got nearly a hundred years of winners. Alysheba was ridden by Chris McCarran, another Hall-of-Famer who has hung up his saddle to manage Santa Anita Park. Matter a fact, the 'After Affirmed Stakes' should be run at Santa Anita. Almost all of these horses have been there; some once, some were based out of there, and any horse that hasn't run in front of the purple backdrop of mountains should at least once, even if it's in heaven."

"Because that's where the Dream Race is run." I used my most dramatic thespian voice.

"Amen, brother," and Leonard played along.

Sometimes when Leonard talked I would forget I was at work and writing a story. I had to quickly scribble down these last nuggets of information as Leonard moved on to the next horse.

"The last few years gave us several near misses as it seems every year we get another horse ready to take the third step to greatness only to sample disappointment. I guess if you had to give an award to an owner who has been so close and always been so classy that would have to go to Mr. Bob Lewis and his wife, Beverly. They may well be the nicest people in all of racing and they would be the only owner who would have two horses racing in the "After Affirmed Stakes".

"Two horses, ouch."

"You'd never know it by lookin' at their faces. They are always polite and friendly to everyone at the track. They

don't know me from Adam, but that never stopped them from saying hello whenever I bumped into them. Keep in mind, some people never win one of the Classics. They came as close as possible; twice being one victory short of the Triple Crown."

I waited for the names of the horses. Leonard knew I had no clue who he was talking about, but he loved the little mental game of hide and seek. He would give me clues, which began subtle enough and grew into embarrassing flashing lights, if I couldn't get it.

"Yeah, the name sure fit the big chestnut and of course the little gray horse's name fit just right too."

My perfectly blank face told Leonard everything he needed to know and now he could get back to his story.

"Silver Charm was a storybook horse. His gray coat was turning more and more silver with each race and with Gary Stevens on board it looked like somebody in Hollywood was making a movie or somethin'."

"Oh, yeah, Silver Charm would have to be in the race." Why did I say that? I don't know, but Leonard was gracious

enough to not embarrass me any further. I guess he figured I did a pretty good job of it all on my own.

"Course now, you know in the Olympics the Silver medal is for second place. Maybe it was just a foretellin', but silver came in second in the Belmont to gold, Touch Gold."

"And that was a tough one." Gee willakers, I sounded as if I was there. Is there any way to unplug this stupid tongue of mine? It's pretty bad, when you even sound stupid to yourself.

"Well, it makes you wonder if the second time around was harder on the Lewises than the first time."

"Yeah, with . . .on . . . what was his name, again?" Well, I had finally done it. I had verbally dug a hole with my mouth and Leonard was enjoying watching me sink into it.

"You mean the horse filled with charisma?" Leonard threw me a lifeline; but if you've never seen or used one before, how do you tell the difference between a lifeline and noose?

"Oh yeah, Filled With Charisma. Now, he was a great one." The first clue to my blunder was Leonard instantly spitting out his chewing tobacco before he choked in the midst of laughter. He was always polite not to make fun of my lack of thoroughbred knowledge, but it was different when I was doing it to myself.

"I think you mean Charismatic. Filled-With-Charisma is probably in his first foal crop." After wiping his mouth it was time to reload his chaw. He looked at me as if to explain his sudden expulsion of his chew. "I gotta find a new brand, this stuff doesn't hold it's flavor like it should." Leonard was the gentleman as he offered me some amnesty from my own embarrassing self-entrapment.

"Charismatic, yes of course."

"Of course." Leonard checked me out to see if I was going to be sick as if I was the one who just swallowed a mouthful of tobacco juice. "Big, beautiful chestnut; gotta be honest, to look at that horse reminded me of lookin' at Secretariat more than any other horse I've seen at the track in the past thirty years. Of course, there's only one Secretariat."

"Of course." A short reply acknowledging Leonard's comment seemed to be the best way of keeping my foot out of my mouth.

"Sometimes horse racing brings out the strangest of emotions. This is just between you and me, but I have cried a handful of times at the track. I cried when Secretariat won the Triple Crown at the Belmont, a couple years later I cried at the same track when Ruffian broke down in the match race against Foolish Pleasure, and I cried when Lemon Drop Kid beat Charismatic in the Belmont. I watched the television back in the barn area and saw what the world saw; the Lewises were disappointed, but they were still smiling as if they had won. Maybe they were crying inside. They're classy people and I can't say if I was sad Charismatic lost or because I wanted the horse's owners to win. I guess separating a horse from the owner isn't so cut and dry. Often, they are one and the same. Either way, a lot of people wanted it for the Lewises feeling they deserved it. Fortunately or unfortunately, as the case may be; in this business nobody gets anything simply because they deserve it. Even without a crown to their credit, they're still special people with more than one special horse."

"Yeah, I guess if it was that easy everybody would own a Triple Crown winner." I mumbled to fill in Leonard's momentary silence.

"Son, there have been a lot of close calls recently and nothing could emphasize the different worlds of racing more than the last five horses needing only the Belmont to win the Triple Crown. Two of 'em were owned by international billionaires; one from Japan who paid $4 million for his yearling, Fashichi Pegasus, and the other an Arab sheik who paid a million dollars for War Emblem just weeks before the Derby. These two groups had unlimited money to buy whatever they wanted. The other three horses are Real Quiet, Funny Cide, and Smarty Jones. Real Quiet was nipped at the wire by Victory Gallop, making Real Quiet the closest of all the horses after Affirmed to wear the crown. Real Quiet was trained by Bob Bafford and owned by Mike Pegram. While Mr. Bafford became a regular in the winner's circle of the biggest races; Mr. Pegram was fairly new to the race game. He bought good horses and made the most of his investment, not too bad for a guy who used to sell hamburgers."

"Hamburgers? You're kidding, right?"

"He had a few McDonald's franchises."

"No kidding."

"And Funny Cide is even more amazing 'cause this horse is owned by a bunch of guys who went to high school together. They played it off as if they didn't have two nickels between 'em as they drove an old yellow school bus right up in the middle of all the limousines. Got to hand it to those dudes, they have a lot of nerve and the whole world could relate to those guys. Funny Cide and his owners scored a victory for the little guy. It was a classic match up of blue blood versus blue collar. Empire Maker was by Unbridled a top stallion and former Derby winner with a pedigree filled with thoroughbred royalty coming and goin' from every direction. Empire Maker's dam was the only living mare to produce four stakes winners. His pedigree is as good as they get. Yeah, I saw him win the Florida Derby as Jerry Bailey hand rode him to win by more than ten lengths. Right before the Derby he beat Funny Cide in the Wood Memorial. If one of these two horses had a shot at racing immortality, before the Derby, it would have been Empire Maker. Funny Cide dominated the Preakness without Empire Maker in the race. Yet, in the mud at Belmont

The Dream Race

the gelding came up short against Empire Maker. However, Funny Cide was still the people's favorite and he's the one in the After Affirmed Stakes."

"I remember all the commotion about Smarty Jones." I said as if I had to show Leonard that I knew something about horse racing.

"Yes sir, it was at Pimlico where Smarty Jones turned more doubters into believers in less than two minutes. His eleven lengths win set the record for the widest margin ever in the Preakness. We're talking about a race that had been run for almost a hundred thirty years since a horse named Preakness won the first Maryland Jockey Club's stakes race. The next year the race was called the Preakness after its first winner. The first time the race was called the Preakness it was won by Survivor by ten lengths. That ten-length margin of victory was a Preakness record for hundred twenty-eight races; until Smarty Jones ran away from the field. By the time the Belmont rolled around Smarty was the biggest favorite in the history of the race and why not, he was undefeated and looking to be only the second horse to be undefeated while earning the Triple Crown." Leonard paused and could tell by the look on my face I had no idea who the first one was. "Seattle Slew."

"Seattle Slew?" I replied.

"Yeah, you were wondering who the undefeated Triple Crown winner was." Sometimes I could swear Leonard could read my mind, either that or I had the worst poker-face on the planet. "The whole world seemed to be of the persuasion that Smarty was going to join Slew as the second one; but the long shot, Birdstone, put on a big surge in the homestretch. Birdstone's the latest horse from the same Whitney family who gave us the filly Regret in 1915; they have been horse racing royalty for a hundred years. There were tears shed as the crowd stood in silent shock. In a classy gesture, Mary Lou Whitney whose parties are legendary celebrations in the sport apologized for spoiling the festivities. She knew as well as any one what another Triple Crown would mean to the world of horse racing. The Belmont was supposed to be a formality. Miss Penny, Secretariat's owner was there to kick off the celebration in the winner's circle, but again it was another year to wait-until-next-year."

After a moment I asked, "Is that the whole field?"

98

After Affirmed

"Yeah, I think that is all of them. There have been other solid contenders since '78, but they didn't win the first two jewels in the crown. If I could include one more horse, I'd take the Seattle Slew colt, Swale. He was a monster and could have been great. He won the Derby, but lost the Preakness. Unlike the other horses in the field, Swale won the Belmont. His win gave trainer Woody Stevens his record setting fourth consecutive Belmont Stakes win during a streak that ran to five. Swale died only days after winning the Belmont. It was one more time when your love for the horses rips at your heart."

Leonard had given me the field to another of the Dream Races. The After Affirmed Stakes would be a good race with top horses who were all so close to grabbing the title of greatness. Any one of them could have been the twelfth Triple Crown winner with a little luck, different weather or track conditions, or maybe if somebody had just been a little more careful with a safety pin. The puzzle for more than a quarter century hasn't been the lack of great horses, as much as it has been too many high quality horses tangling in the same years. Like the twenty-five years after Citation in '48 until Secretariat in '73, it was not a time without great horses; it was merely a time between crowns and as for now, the question remains, who will wear the next crown after Affirmed?

The Dream Race

Global Gauntlet: Racing is by no stretch an American innovation. Europe was racing on the turf long before the colonies revolted. Today, racing is firmly planted in the Far East and Australia, the Middle East, all over Europe including France and Italy, Canada and South America. One of the greatest of all the international horses was the New Zealand born Phar Lap.

Global Gauntlet

"So, you want to know about the greatest ever?" Leonard's question was strange based upon the fact that we had been discussing the topic pretty much non-stop all day long.

"Yeah, I thought that's what we were talking about."

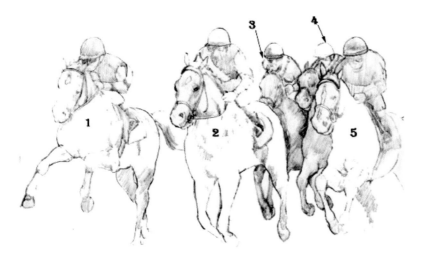

Global Gauntlet

1. Phar Lap
2. Nijinsky II
3. Ribot
4. Shergar
5. Sea Bird

"You ever notice how baseball calls its championship the World Series and it only has teams from the United States. Bet you never thought of that, have ya?"

"What about the '93 Toronto BlueJays?" I asked.

"I thought you weren't a big sports fan."

"What can I say, I recently bought the Encyclopedia of Baseball. Hey, I'm a sports writer!" I joked as I pounded my chest like Tarzan.

Leonard smiled and proceeded. "It's the same with any sport in the states. If we play it, then the winner is the world champion . . . even if they never left the good ole U. S. of A. Americans are funny that way, but make no doubt about it; we are the same way about horses and probably have less reason to be than sports like baseball, basketball, and football. Those sports either started here or are played exclusively here; but the same can't be said about horses."

"Leonard, I'm not exactly sure I know what you mean."

"That proves my point." Leonard punctuated his remark with a deliberate spit of tobacco. "Of course you don't

The Dream Race

know what I mean; you are so accustomed to the fishbowl you live in that you don't even realize that there's a whole ocean out there filled with horses."

"You mean an ocean filled with fish. You're mixing your metaphors." I said glibly, still humored by my mock declaration of being a sportswriter.

"OK, let's say an ocean full of seahorses, if it makes you feel better . . . and you, young man, are correcting your elders. I wouldn't make a habit of it." Leonard winked, but he still expected more respect and less adolescent wit.

"Leonard, I'm sorry." He nodded in acceptance of my apology. "So, tell me about these seahorses."

"Well, let me ask you a question, kind of a pop quiz."

"OK," I braced myself for another humbling experience.

"When I say, 'the Derby', what do you think of?"

"That's easy; the Kentucky Derby."

"Uh-huh."

"Well, did I pass the test?"

"That depends . . ."

"What does it depend on?" I asked.

"It depends on whether you are in a fishbowl or the ocean. If you're just in the fishbowl, you're right."

"And if I'm in the ocean . . ."

"You're half right."

"Half right?" I replied.

"Yeah, at best half right; 'cause in some parts of the ocean you would be eaten alive for that answer."

"OK, preferring not to be eaten alive; let's leave the fishbowl. Can you tell me what you are talking about?"

"Well, it all gets back to Americans thinking that if you are the best here, then you're the best everywhere on the planet. The Derby, and I emphasize the word 'THE'; is really a reference to the original Derby, which they've run for over 200 years in England, the Epsom Derby."

"You mentioned the Epsom Derby when we talked about Eclipse."

"That's right, you can't really talk about horse racing without talking about England. And you sure can't talk about thoroughbreds without taking a close look at the whole ocean; not just England. There have been significant contributions to racing and the breed from all over Europe and the rest of the world. Since you want to talk about the greatest horse ever, I think you might be talking about more than just the best horse in the fishbowl; even if it's a mighty big fishbowl." Leonard winked again, acknowledging his intentional mixing of metaphors and I wasn't about to correct him.

"All right, let's hear more about the world's best horses or should I say the ocean's best seahorses?"

"We'll stay on dry land for a while. Thoroughbreds have typically raced on one side of the Atlantic or the other. In the states the Triple Crown races are the most famous with the Kentucky Derby being the most famous of the bunch. It's almost funny to think of the Derby on this side of the pond being almost a hundred years younger than the Derby on that

side. Talking about the Derby in England is a whole different topic all by itself. England's racing dominance on that side of the Atlantic has been challenged by other European countries. There is a new kid on the block so to speak in Europe; it's the Arc de Triomphe run at Longchamps, near Paris, France. There may be more of a rivalry between the horses on both sides of the English Channel than there is between horses on both sides of the Atlantic. While only connoisseurs of racing in this country have any idea of what happens in European racing, the rivalry between the horses from various European countries is much more heated. National pride is at stake any time a horse travels across the English Channel; be it a French horse in England or an English horse in France, it matters."

"Are telling me that a horse knows if he's French or English, or even Swahili for that matter?" I asked; interrupted is more accurate.

"The horse might not, but the people screaming at the top of their lungs in the stands, they know; and that much you can count on. You see racing in other parts of the world is more like World Cup Soccer than the World Series in Baseball. We generally don't even know who's playing in the World

Cup; while over there you'd get looked at like you were from another planet, if you didn't know who was playing; much less have a favorite team. The reputation of English Soccer fans is well earned as being the most passionate sports fans in the world. The last place you want to be is in the middle of one of those international football, as they call it, crowds when they go crazy."

"Yeah, I've seen pictures and heard stories about them. Passionate is a polite way of putting it, crazy is probably a better description."

"Well, boy, you have to understand those are the same people who love their horses the same way they love their soccer teams. Candidly, there's only one thing they like less than losing a football match and that's when their four-legged champions don't get the respect they deserve." Leonard said.

I waited and waited, but Leonard was letting his silence accent his statement. His silence was more sanitary than his nasty habit of spitting tobacco as a substitute for punctuation.

"Remember when we talked about Ribot? He was perfect, undefeated. He even won the Arc twice. Imagine winning the biggest race on this side of the Atlantic two times against the best competition in the world. Sixteen races and sixteen victories against nothin' but the best."

"If you hadn't told me about him, I'd never have heard of him." I said.

"Gotta be honest with you; if I hadn't seen him in Kentucky as a stud, I probably wouldn't have really understood what he was all about. The sight of him was like a giant fishnet scooping me right out of the fishbowl. Yeah, that was when I learned about the 'fish' in the ocean. Son, there's some mighty dang good fish on the other side of the ocean."

"What was Ribot doing in Kentucky?"

"America may be a fishbowl, but we do have a lot of people whose goal is to breed the best horses in the world. The best way to do that is to bring the best horses in the world to our fishbowl." Leonard waited a moment as if to clear his thoughts. "Ribot was bred by one of the greatest horsemen ever, Federico Tesio, of Italy. Tesio bred and raced some of the greatest horses Europe ever saw. His stallions have a lasting legacy in about every championship on the track over

the last fifty years and still today. Tesio never saw Ribot race. The old man passed away when Ribot was just a yearling, but before he died he said Ribot was going to be special. For a man who had bred two other undefeated champions; his definition of special was probably a little more 'special' than others."

"One thing racing has in common on both sides of the pond as the Brits say, is that breeders were typically very wealthy. Tesio, while he wasn't hurting for money was unusual in that he had a financial partner. It's a testament to Tesio's abilities as a breeder to think he may have started a new trend in the industry as horse racing changed from being a hobby for rich gentlemen into a profession. While there had been professional trainers, there really hadn't been a professional breeder. Tesio's a pioneer as a full time breeder. He turned the art of breeding into a science. His hunches for mating the right stallion to the right mare went well beyond guesswork. Even more amazing was the ability of his stallions to pass these traits on to their get. Generations of horses have passed and still Tesio's pedigrees continue to resurface at all the major races around the world."

"His babies are all around the world?"

"Yeah, that's right. That's why Mr. Gaines leased Ribot."

"Leased him? You can do that?"

"Funny thing; Mr. Gaines paid $1,300,000 to lease the horse for five years. That was $100,000 more than the record paid for the great Nashua five years before. Once Ribot got to Gainesway Farm he became a fixture and stayed nearly a dozen years instead of the five originally agreed upon. I bet you had no idea that an Italian played such a major role in the development of the thoroughbred breed or the racing industry, much less our fishbowl here in the states."

"An Italian? I had no idea."

"Like I said the world of racing could almost be divided into three geographic fishbowls: the United States, England, and the rest of the world. You could talk all day long about the history of racing in England and its great champions for over three-hundred years. It's places like Italy and the rest of Europe that don't get their due. That may be why the Arc in France is so highly regarded. It is a jewel in the crown of this

The Dream Race

emerging fishbowl known as the rest of the world. Japan has emerged as a major player worldwide in racing. The Middle East has made major strides in becoming a dominant force in racing and they have been doing it in all three fishbowls. For the past ten to twenty years, all the classics have had their share of Arabian owned horses. And maybe the best of them all was actually a horse from New Zealand."

"New Zealand? Leonard, you have to be pulling my leg, right?"

"No sir, New Zealand may have produced the greatest horse ever to race in the third fishbowl."

"Who's that?"

"Phar Lap. He raced almost all of his races in Australia becoming a living legend during his day; maybe the most beloved horse any country had ever seen. Needless to say, Australian racing didn't get a lot of credit with the folks back in the states or in Jolly Ole England. There was only one way the big chestnut could prove his greatness and that was to come over to the states to race on a bigger stage."

"Bigger fishbowl?" I asked.

"Yeah exactly, he came over here in 1932, but ironically he couldn't race in the United States. When he arrived gambling on horses was illegal in California, so he was raced in Tijuana, Mexico at the famous Caliente race track. He won so easily that he converted everyone who saw him demolish the competition. Too bad he never got the chance to convince the rest of the world."

"Why not?"

"Good question. No one really knows what happened. It's still a mystery. After the race Phar Lap was shipped to the San Francisco Bay area. A couple of days later Phar Lap died of what's been called accidental poisoning. Others have regarded the tragedy as a much more sinister act pointing fingers at a wide range of shady characters. Phar Lap may have been just a horse, but say that to someone from New Zealand or Australia and you'd better be prepared to defend yourself. Phar Lap's death hit the people from his homeland like a punch to the stomach. You know, good race horses have their hooves buried as a tribute; great horses are buried whole as an even greater tribute. That ain't nothing compared to Phar Lap; his stuffed body is on permanent display in a museum in

Melbourne, Australia for all the world to see and remember forever. Man, that's love."

"OK, I can see the favorite son was loved, but was he that good?"

"Not at first, he only won once in his first nine races; then something happened. He couldn't lose once he hit his stride, winning almost 95% of his next 35 races. These two eyes never saw him run, but those who did will tell you without any hesitation that Phar Lap was the best horse they ever saw. I'll tell you one of them was Mr. Charlie Whittingham, one of the greatest trainers of all time. Mr. Charlie was there at the Aqua Caliente Handicap in '32. If he said Phar Lap was the best he had seen, I'd be dumb as a rock to argue with him. You know, 'aqua caliente' means 'hot water' in Spanish. Let me tell ya, Phar Lap boiled the water in this fishbowl."

"That's incredible to think someone would harm a horse for what, money?" The words were no sooner out of my mouth before I finished my own thought. "Yeah, I guess money will do strange things to people. I still can't believe it."

"What if I told you another one of the greatest horses of all time met an even more devious end for political reasons?"

"Leonard, that's frightening. What are talking about?"

"Just one of the best horses out of the UK in the past twenty-five years. Some people will tell you Shergar was the best horse of his generation. He won the Epsom Derby and had a charmed race career, that is, until his fairy-tale turned into a nightmare."

"What happened?"

"No one really knows for sure. It's horse racing's equivalent to the disappearance of Jimmy Hoffa. No one knows what happened. There are a lot of rumors, but it sure seems Shergar was kidnapped."

"Kidnapped? Somebody kidnapped a horse? Why?"

"I don't know if it was for money or not, most rumors say it was political and connect the kidnapping to the Irish Republican Army."

"The IRA, you can't be serious." I was shocked by what I was hearing.

The Dream Race

"That's right and like I said, no one knows what happened to the horse after he disappeared. After he disappeared everyone waited day by day for the horse to be returned or a ransom note, but it never happened and not so much as a clue turned up. Some people say they have information about Shergar, but after more than twenty years the answers haven't been found and neither has Shergar."

"How good was Shergar?"

"In some strange way, his kidnapping suggests just how important he was. I mean nobody kidnaps a plow-horse. We have an idea how good Shergar was on the track, but the shame of it is that we'll never know how good a stallion he could have been. He had a great pedigree with the blood of Northern Dancer, a stallion whose legend has grown more and more with each generation producing more winners. Shergar was owned by the Aga Khan. This is a royal family from India. The grandfather of the current Aga Khan was talked into racing in England because he was told if he wanted to be taken seriously, England is where he had to race and race he did."

"Again, the bigger fishbowl theory."

"You got it. The Aga Khan bred and raced the finest of horses through the early part of the twentieth century. He really is royalty in the sport of kings. Aga Khan is joined by Federico Tesio as two of the strongest influences in racing during the middle of the twentieth century. When the Aga Khan was introduced to the English racing scene, no one could ever have guessed the impact his family's horses would have on racing for the next hundred years. One can only imagine what Shergar's Northern Dancer's blood could have added to history and the breed. The physical likeness between the two was amazing. Shergar's blaze down the center of his forehead was almost identical the way it tucked into his nostrils."

"Leonard, you seem more than a little partial to Northern Dancer. Why is that?"

"He was maybe the best bred horse ever. His two grandsires might be the two greatest producers of all time. Nearco, another of Tesio's undefeated stallions, whose blood seems to be in almost every stakes winning pedigree. Native Dancer was the other grandsire. His lineage is better known in this country and every bit as impressive as Nearco's. Think

about this; between Nearco and Native Dancer they only have one loss."

"Wow," So, much for my extensive verbal skills. Hey, I'm a writer not a speaker.

"I'd have a hard time picking between those two. Two great race horses and both are great sires and all that blood flows through Northern Dancer. His win at the '64 Kentucky Derby proved he could run. It's what he did in the stud barn that took him from our fishbowl and proved he could swim in the world's ocean. Then again, he had the best blood on both sides of the Atlantic. He did his part to keep all three fishbowls stocked with champions."

"What do you mean?"

"Well, the little stallion produced winners around the world. He may be more famous for his European legacy. The most famous of the bunch may be Nijinsky. He confirmed Northern Dancer's potential as a sire and that's a good thing when it's your first foal crop."

"I get the connection, Northern Dancer – Nijinsky, but what did Nijinsky do that was so incredible?" I asked.

"You've heard about the two long spells without a Triple Crown winner in the states; after Citation in '48 and after Affirmed in '78. Those streaks ran for at least twenty-five years. Imagine a similar streak with the European equivalent of the Triple Crown, except the streak in England lasted closer to forty years. Nijinsky did what many were beginning to believe was impossible; winning the Two Thousand Guineas at Newmarket, the Epsom Derby, and the St. Leger. Nijinsky's English Triple Crown in 1970 turned up the interest in finding our next crown winner over here. Talk about a horse jumping out of the fishbowl. Nijinsky was actually bred in Canada and sold at auction. He was then shipped over to Ireland. Nijinsky went on to be the first winner of the Epsom Derby bought at auction. After his racing career was over he was brought back to Kentucky and stood at Claiborne Farms. That's where I saw him. He was a tall rangy animal. He looked at you with eyes that said, 'What are you looking at?' Oh, yeah, I had to go back and look at his Daddy. Northern Dancer was at least a hand smaller. Nijinsky was an elegant beast. Funny thing, even though he was foaled in Canada he wasn't named until he was in Ireland." Leonard chuckled.

The Dream Race

"Yeah, what's so funny about that?"

"Well, he was the first Nijinsky over there, but he wasn't the first Nijinsky over here. When he came back to the states he had to pick up the Roman numeral two after his name."

"That's like having a homecoming party and having everybody ask what your name is," I said.

"Twain, you sure have imagination," Coming from Leonard, the inventor of the Dream Race that was quite a compliment.

"So, who else is swimming in this international fishbowl?" My question added to Leonard's entertainment.

"Good question. There's too many horses to name them all. I could list dozens of Epsom Derby winners or dozens of Arc de' Triomphe winners, but if I had to single one out for the fishbowl it would have to be Sea-Bird." Leonard was obviously pleased with his pun as he laughed a little harder while slapping me on the back.

"OK, I get it: all this talk about oceans and fishbowls wouldn't be complete without a horse named Sea-Bird."

"That's right. I guess you walked right into that one."

"Well, other than his name; does he really deserve to be put in the company of most elite horses of all time?"

"Honestly, I'm not an expert on European racing . . . so, I'll have to go along with what the experts over there said. When Europe ranked their top one-hundred race horses, Sea-Bird was called the Horse-of-the-Century. Man o' War took the same title over here. That's a pretty hefty compliment; but keep in mind, Sea-Bird is one of a very select group to win the premier race in two different fishbowls. I guess the only thing to top that would be one horse winning the top race in all three fishbowls."

"You mean the Kentucky Derby, the Epsom Derby, and Arc de'Triomphe?"

"Yeah, two Derbies, and an Arc: that would be truly amazing," as Leonard spoke I could see the wheels turning in his head. "Amazing because of the geography of racing in three different countries on two continents?"

"Not just that, but think about this. The winner would have to be equally great on the turf and on the dirt, plus the Arc runs clockwise. May not sound like much, but a horse trains his whole life to make left turns and suddenly he's asked to do something different and still do it better than everyone else. Yeah, that would have to be a special horse."

"Sea-Bird, huh?"

"Yeah that's right. Think about this, with all the horses being flown around in private jets, it isn't impossible to see a horse come along that can compete successfully in all three fishbowls. I guess the greatest horse of all time may be on a plane someplace right now preparing for two Derbies and the Arc. You know, when the twentieth century started there was no such thing as the Triple Crown. Maybe the Derbies and the Arc will someday be the Triple Crown of the twenty-first century. When that happens maybe that will stop the debate; but until that time, I still have to go with four sea horses and one Sea-Bird."

The Dream Race

Iron Horses: Durability is the synonym of 'Iron Horse'. These are the horses that spent long careers at the track. They ran seventy, eighty, a hundred, or even as many as a hundred-thirty races during their careers.

Iron Horses

It had to be late afternoon. I normally put my watch on first thing in the morning, but I had met Leonard for breakfast an hour or two before 'the-first-thin-in-the-morning'. Besides, Leonard had warned me not to look at my watch when he was

Iron Horses

1. Armed
2. Kelso
3. Stymie
4. Exterminator
5. Forego
6. Cigar
7. John Henry

talking; so, maybe subconsciously I forgot it on purpose. Whatever the reason I had no idea what the actual time was and I wasn't about to ask Leonard. Fortunately, the day had flown by as he shared story after story with me. As I reviewed the chores accomplished and the events of the day, there was no doubt that it had been a good nine hour work day. The labor had been more exhilarating than draining. I checked my hands. They were way past the blister stage. A deep splinter right in the palm would have probably made them feel better. Again, as with being tired, the sting in my hands felt good in a strange kind of way. I looked at the glowing pink with a sense of pride. Remember, for a city kid who thought 'dirt' was something you read in the gossip column, this day on the farm was an education in more ways than one.

Lunch was more than four or five hours ago. That being the case it had to be almost time to call it a day, right?

"Hey, Twain, let's break to get a coke." Leonard was really getting used to calling me by my new moniker.

"Fine with me."

"Yeah, we'll have time to get the rest of this done when we get back."

"Get back? You mean, you want me to come back tomorrow?"

"Well, boy, that's entirely up to you. I don't mind the help and the conversation has been pretty fair as well."

"Are you talking about coming back here today?" I asked.

"Well, you do want to get a full day in, don't you?"

Hey, it's not that I'm afraid to put in a full day's work. OK, maybe it is. I don't really know, because before today my definition of a full day's work was something a little bit less than what I was currently experiencing. I guess the scary part was like being Columbus as he sailed into waters where no one had ever been before. I mean this ten hour work day was already uncharted territory for me. I mean if a person could work ten hours, did that mean that eleven, twelve, or even worse could be possible. I had done a pretty good job all day not letting Leonard know how green I was at being a redneck. Suddenly, the sting of my open blisters were more obvious.

The discomfort was now pain. Earlier, I had spit in my palm and rubbed the sting away. So, I tried that ancient Chinese secret again; this time I had more tears than saliva. It is hard to keep going when you think you've already reached the finish line. I was doing fine, until I realized I had no idea where the finish line was. My day's work, which was becoming a labor of love instantly reverted back into merely labor.

"Full day? Yeah, of course . . . we're just getting started, right, Leonard? I could do this all day and night." I was petrified at what Leonard had in mind and what really concerned me was his inability to contain his laughter. He's trying to kill me! And he thinks it's funny!

"Boy, you're hysterical."

"I'm glad I could entertain you." My pained reply brought Leonard's arm up and around my shoulder.

"OK, a Coca-Cola and I'm buying." He said.

"No, my treat, I insist 'cause I'm putting this on an expense report. Let Mr. Williams pay for it."

Iron Horses

"Sounds good to me. I'll tell you about the Iron Horses."

"Who are they?"

"Well Twain, those are the ones that got up early and never went home."

"Does that make me an Iron Horse?" It seemed to be a natural segue, one that Leonard was hinting towards.

"Yeah, if you keep it up for the rest of your career, maybe then you'll be an Iron Horse."

"You mean like Joe DiMaggio?" I asked. Leonard gave me a glare before he could even laugh.

"Some sports writer you are. DiMaggio was the Yankee Clipper; Lou Gerhig was the Iron Horse."

"I'll be careful to get the names straight, if I ever interview one of them."

"If you do, be sure to ask them about the Dream Race." Leonard said.

"How's that? Have you told them about the Dream Race?"

"Let me ask you a question. Where's the Dream Race?" Leonard was testing me.

"Heaven . . .?"

"Yeah, well when you speak with them be sure to ask 'em if they were at the Dream Race. Have you done many interviews with an OUIJA board?"

"Yeah, I knew that . . . hey, Leonard, don't I owe you a soda while you tell me about the 'Iron Horses'." A quick change of subject seemed like the best exit from the corner I had backed myself into.

"OK, here's the deal; Lou Gerhig's called the Iron Horse because he played in over two-thousand baseball games in a row; 2,130 to be exact. That's fourteen years without takin' a day off. The Iron Horses on the track are the ones that started race after race, year after year. So many horses go right to the breeding shed after their three year old season. The Iron Horses kept running, not always winning; but always running."

The Dream Race

We moved outside. I wasn't sure if it was warmer or cooler outside. The sun felt warmer, but the wind was refreshingly cool. Either way, it was a nice change.

"There' something different about the Iron Horses, kind of funny too." Leonard said.

"What's that?"

"Well, when the trains were first run through the west, the Indians referred to them as Iron Horses. Then, the term started getting used for other durable contraptions, even people. Now, to refer to the Iron Horses of racing is really a throwback reference to the trains. There's one other thing. Trains ran on rails, not dirt. The Iron Horses in the Dream Race, don't run on the dirt either."

"Turf?" I asked.

"Good boy, at least I know you have been listening to some of what I've said." He punched me in the shoulder. He could tell I was hanging on every word, but neither of us was going to admit it.

"So, Leonard, where would this Dream Race be?"

"The Iron Horses would have to run on the turf at the Fair Grounds in New Orleans."

"OK, but is there any reason why New Orleans?" I knew there had to be, nothing about Leonard's Dream Race seemed to be left to chance.

"Well, since the Iron Horses are a tribute to longevity, there really are only a few places that would be appropriate; New Orleans or Saratoga."

"And New Orleans gets the nod?" I said or asked as the case may be.

"That's right. New Orleans came first. The Union Race Course in New Orleans is the oldest site of racing in this country. That's where the Fair Ground track is now. There were a couple other tracks in Louisiana before Union opened, but they're long gone. The Fair Grounds course has been the site of racing going back more than a hundred-fifty years. The Civil War and changes in the law have closed the track for several years. The Iron Horses would have run at Old Metairie, but it's a graveyard."

"You mean it's closed?"

"No, I mean it's a cemetery."

"Oh, sorry, go ahead"

"The Fair Grounds has tried to keep the old Southern plantation feel. During the War Between the States almost all the old plantation homes in the area where burned down. Ironically, the track was called Union Park and the Union Troops turned it into one of their camps; otherwise it would have probably met a similar fate to the other tracks and plantation homes. Racing may have stopped, but the track for the most part was spared."

Without saying a word I scribbled down every word. Just as I caught up Leonard continued.

"You see, to be an Iron Horse doesn't mean everything is always perfect. On the contrary, almost all the Iron Horses had to overcome their own adversity. Many of them had time off the track due to injury, but they kept coming back; just like the track at the Fair Grounds."

When I caught up again I was speechless. I looked at Leonard and could sense emotions I hadn't felt before. When

he was ready and with no provocation from me whatsoever, he went on.

"Saratoga is still pretty much along the original design. The flowing peaks make a silhouette that sticks in your brain. You only have to see it one time and you'll never forget it. I'd probably upset a lot of folks over in Louisville by saying this, but even the spires at Churchill Downs had taken a peek at Saratoga for some inspiration. Saratoga didn't invent the spire, but they did bring 'em to racing. You see the South was the hotbed of racing up until the Civil War. After the war, the South wasn't left as the leader of much of anything. Horses were one of the great assets of the South. The Union soldiers wrote letters talking 'bout the horses ridden by the Confederates. They were pretty darn envious of those Southern horses. Aiken, South Carolina might have become the Mecca for racing in this country; but when the country split that ended that."

"So, the thoroughbred was actually bigger in the South before the North."

"Son, not just the thoroughbred; the Union officers made special reference to the horses floating over the ground.

The Dream Race

They said the confederates could ride with guns in both hands and none on the horse. The Tennessee Walking horse didn't become a breed until the 1920s when a bunch of folks got together to start a specific breed based upon that special floating trot. One thing's for sure, those horses were the descendants of the plantation horses that later charged across the battlefields. Southerners loved their horses."

"Now, a lot of them just love horse power." My comment made Leonard look at me funny. "You know, NASCAR!"

"Yeah, I guess you could say that, but I think there's something more beautiful about one to one horse power that you just don't get from hundreds of gasoline powered ones . . . anyhow after the war, Saratoga took the lead from places like New Orleans and Aiken as horse power shifted from the south to the north; but remember, the Iron Horse race is about durability and longevity. Speakin' of horse power . . ." Leonard said as he popped open the door to his old truck.

"This is my Iron Horse; lots of miles on this old baby."

"How many?"

"Some as many as a hundred."

"Are we talking horse power again or are you talking about a hundred thousand miles?" I said, pulling with a mighty tug to get the passenger door closed.

"Nah, a hundred races."

"A hundred races?"

"Today, a lot of the best horses retire after a dozen races, maybe less."

"And the Iron Horses raced a hundred times?"

"Some did, others were real close."

"Who had the most?"

"A horse named Stymie . . . 131 starts." Leonard said.

"I take it that's a lot."

"When you figure most horses may run ten times in a year; it would take thirteen years to equal Stymie's record. Even if they ran twenty races a year, it would still take 'em six or seven years to catch the ole boy. You know when Lou Gehrig set the record for consecutive ball games, most folks

said it was the one record that would never be broken. Then, Cal Ripken came along and broke the original Iron Horse's record; but I say no horse is gonna break Stymie's record."

"How good was he?"

"Good enough to win more money than any other horse during his days on the track. It was a record he took from another Iron Horse, Armed."

"Was Armed any good? I know he didn't win the Triple Crown, but did he win any of those races?"

"Son, how many times am I going to have to tell you; the Triple Crown is a great accomplishment; but it isn't the only measuring stick to put to a horse's career on the track?"

"Two, maybe three more times ought to do it . . . just kidding." I was ready to duck in case Leonard threw something. "OK, minus the Triple Crown races, was Armed any good or not?"

"Well, Armed was the 1947 Horse-of-the-Year for Calumet. As a matter of fact, Armed held the record for career earnings for all of seventeen days, but his real claim to fame

would have to be when he beat the 1946 Triple Crown winner, Assault. It was one of the great match races of all-time. Two things to remember: first, horses don't get match races with Triple Crown winners unless they're special."

"And number two?"

"Number two, Armed kicked Assault's can, that's what he did and did it by eight lengths. In the process Armed took the Horse-of-the-Year honors away from Assault the reining Horse-of-the-Year." Leonard was emphatic.

"Out of curiosity, why did these owners keep running these Iron Horses? Couldn't they breed them?"

"That's a good guess. Armed didn't pan out as a stallion, so he went back to the track. But, let me give you another reason: money! Stymie cost only $1,500 and during his career he won almost a million. Most of the Iron Horses are geldings or have other breeding problems, but Stymie was actually a pretty good stallion on top of everything else. The one thing geldings are good for is running at the track. After that, they just eat and makes the stuff you put in the wheel barrow all day.

"Lucky guys, get to eat all day, lounge around, and have someone clean up after you."

"Speakin' of the lucky ones, do you know what a teaser is?" Leonard asked. I guess Leonard didn't want to talk about horses any more.

"Yeah, I've dated more than one." My reply sent Leonard into a real gut buster. I liked making Leonard laugh, but why did I always feel it would ultimately be at my expense?

"I don't think you and I are speaking the same language. A teaser is a horse whose sole role in life is to be the stunt double for expensive stallions; like in Hollywood when the big movie star is about to do something dangerous, they let some other guy get run over by a bus. That's what the teaser does."

"Are bus accidents common on horse farms?"

"Boy, you're too much. Nah, but it can be worse than a bus given the nature of the chore."

"Leonard, exactly what kind of chore does the teaser do?"

"Well, all the kings from the old days had food testers to make sure that no one had poisoned his food."

"Stunt doubles and food testers . . . Leonard could you be a little more specific? What does the teaser do?"

"He's a love tester or even better, he's a stunt stud."

"What?"

"That's right. You see, if a mare doesn't want to be bred, one sure fire way to defend herself is a swift kick right in the boy's privates when he is at his most vulnerable."

"Ouch! Some things never change."

"Yeah, I guess nature equips all females with a certain universal knowledge of self defense against male predators."

"Oh man . . . so, the teaser. . ."

"The teaser's only job on this planet is to find out if the mare is going to kick or hold still. Once the breeder knows the answer to that question, the teaser goes back into his stall."

"Come to think of it, I haven't dated teasers; I am the teaser!" My self-effacing wit had Leonard laughing again.

"Been put back in the stall a few times have you, young man?"

"No, kicked is more like it." I clutched my lower-lower stomach at the thought of thousand pound rejection.

"Now, that you've got the picture, you understand why the teaser may be a five dollar horse, but he's the stunt man for a million dollar star."

"Getting run over by a bus doesn't sound so bad right about now." I paused allowing Leonard the maximum enjoyment of my comedic repartee. "Leonard, why are we talking about teasers? What do they have to do with the Iron Horses?"

"Well, almost a hundred years ago, there was one mighty good horse that spent a lifetime on the track. His name was Roamer. Seems he got his name from the simple fact that somebody jumped a fence. No one's real sure if the mare went lookin' for him or if the teaser broke out for a one-night commando mission; but the result of the unplanned breeding was a horse that could out run about any horse. That's the story of Roamer the 1914 Horse-of-the-Year."

"Well, good for the teaser. I mean after a while the teaser has to develop a complex. You know, he starts to think he's really ugly or something."

"Maybe." Leonard answered.

"Maybe . . . what's that supposed to mean?"

"Maybe the teaser was ugly and the mare just didn't know any better."

"Leonard, you lost me."

"Oh, did I forget to mention Roamer's mother was blind. The teaser could've been a mule and she wouldn't have seen the difference."

The Dream Race

"Goes to prove the old saying, 'even a blind squirrel finds a nut once in a while'."

"True, but would you mind doing me one favor?"

"Yes, what is it?"

"Leave the old sayings to me . . . you never know when you might be using one of mine." Leonard grinned as we pulled up at the diner. That soda was going to taste great. During the course of the day Leonard had told me about a whole day of Dream Races. He told me about the fabulous fillies, the recent horses, and the ancient roots to all thoroughbreds. I couldn't help but wonder when he was going to name the one horse that wins it all. I started out listening to his stories just waiting for the answer to be handed to me. Now, I found myself fascinated with a series of stories and all the details. These were his stories. What I mean is all these stories had a personal side. Leonard was there or he knew someone who was. Well, all of them except the Byerly Turk according to Leonard.

Leonard was not only a living link to horse racing history, but he was also a master of the lost art of story telling.

In an age when the world sits in front of a television, Leonard was the television. He was the voice coming over the radio back in a time when families used to get together in the evening. He was entertainment in its original form; the way Native American tribes passed stories down from generation to generation. This lost art was the source of news to a whole village. The story teller was the person who shaped a culture. If Leonard wanted a monopoly on all the old sayings, fine. It was the least I could do; not to mention the fact, his copyrights were grandfathered over time.

"Sally, a couple of your coldest Cokes and the kid is buying."

"What kind?" replied a woman who could have been Leonard's age.

"Coca-Cola, of course."

"What kind of Coke?" I mumbled.

"See, boy you grew up in a different age. See when me and Sally was knee-high to a grasshopper there was only one kind of Coke. Now, there's too many to keep count, but if you go around places in the South or around folks like us, we just

call 'em all Cokes; then we let someone else sort out which kind. There are orange coke, grape coke, and even strawberry coke. Folks up north call 'em sodas or pop, but down here we call all of 'em cokes. Just like all cameras were called Kodaks and all refrigerators were called Frigidaires."

I was smart enough to realize Leonard always had a reason when he would wonder off on a seemingly insignificant piece of trivia. All I had to do was wait. Sally plopped down a couple of pops, I mean cokes in front of us.

"Yeah, that's good. Some things you can just count on. It's good to know what you were going to get." Leonard took another gulp. "That's the way the Iron Horses were. They may not have been champagne, but man – you could count on those horses and you always knew what you were gonna get. Old Rosebud went to the track 'bout the same time as Roamer. Old Rosebud even won the Kentucky Derby. Here was a horse that beat the best, got injured, and came back. Old Rosebud raced until he was eleven. He raced 80 times and came back from injury three times. He was the real thing. He never quit, he ran his whole life. He even died on the track and no tellin'

how long he might have raced; he won his last race at the age of ten." Leonard took another big swig of his Coke, looked at the classic shape of the glass bottle, shook his head and added, "Couldn't have a race of Iron Horses without Roamer and Old Rosebud; year after year, you always knew what you were gonna get, the real thing."

I was pacing my drink a little slower than Leonard, but then again maybe I was stalling; not knowing exactly how much more work he had in mind for me back at the barn.

"Leonard, that gives us Stymie, Armed, Roamer, and Old Rosebud in the Iron Horses race on the Dream Race card. Any one else?"

The old man's eyes never left the bottle he cradled.

"Well, let's see . . . we have two horses from the '40s and two horses from around 1914 to 1920. Let's talk about one that fell in between; Seabiscuit."

"The one in the movie."

"None other and that horse didn't even start to run until he was almost four. He just laid around all the time and acted

123

mean, but once he started running, he loved it. Some horses are fast and nobody can beat 'em, just because they're so dang fast. Some others are real battlers; they know they're racin' and they plain hate to lose. Then, there're horses like Seabiscuit, man, that horse liked to race. He had more fun racin' than any horse I ever saw. It was a big game to him."

"How many races did Seabiscuit run?"

"Eighty-nine times. Nah, he didn't win 'em all, but he contended every time. You had to be a fool to bet against him, 'cause he was a threat in every race. Already told you about the match race with War Admiral, his uncle; I'll stand on my comment that match races with Triple Crown winners don't happen with lesser horses. War Admiral only ran twenty-six times and he's rightfully considered one of the greatest horses of all-time; but Seabiscuit was an Iron Horse. He loved to run; but when he did, it was all business eighty-nine times."

"Did the public really adore Seabiscuit the way the movie says?"

"Boy, here's a couple things about the American sportsman. First, they like underdogs, second they cheer champions, and third they love any one who gives a hundred percent a hundred percent of the time. When you do all three of these things, you will be the object of public adoration; period."

"That's all it takes to be a public idol." I wasn't testing Leonard's comment as much as putting it to memory for my article.

"Don't you don't believe me? All you need to do is check it out for yourself, look at the rest of the Iron Horses; everyone of them was elevated to the status of your modern day rock stars."

"Like who?"

"In his day Kelso was right there with Elvis. When you are the only five time Horse-of-the-Year, being compared to the King ain't much of a stretch. Kelso's last race was a tear jerker. The crowd knew it was the last time he would run: Mrs. Dupont let him take the rest of his life off. He'd earned it."

"Who else?"

"You're probably old enough to have heard of, or maybe even seen Cigar or John Henry. Now, those two horses kept running and kept winning. Cigar's sixteen race win streak tied Citation with the longest winning streak in the states. When you walk into Gulfstream Park's paddock area the first thing you see is a great big statue of Cigar. Of all the great horses that ran at Gulfstream, he musta been pretty darn good to be the one bronzed for all eternity right in the middle of all those palm trees circling the backside."

The way Leonard could describe a scene was miraculous. He could bring the gift of sight to the blind. Places I had never seen were as clear as sunlight when he told me about them.

"Yeah, Cigar was another of Mr. Paulson's horses. He had plenty of 'em, but no cigar."

"Leonard, is that where that saying comes from?"

"Nah, people have been saying 'no cigar' for years, I think it had to do with winning prizes at the circus. Right or wrong, I don't know, but one thing's for sure 'no cigar', is the best description of about every horse he faced. He may have lost a couple times, but even when he did get beat, the competition was still 'no cigar'. He was special and you had better be when you race in the red, white, and blue of old glory; right on down to the white stars on the blue sleeves. When you talk about a fan favorite; Cigar was one. Imagine the fanfare of a retirement party. Thousands of screaming fans coming out to get one last look at 'their' champion."

"Was it the same with John Henry?"

"As far as what he did on the track, kind of; but not the way it all ended. John Henry was one of the greatest Iron Horses of modern era, but his career ended suddenly just two weeks before the first Breeders' Cup. The horse whose legs were made of steel was human after all . . . that's an interesting choice of words." Leonard was amused by his accidental pun.

"John Henry was a horse that was given up on time and time again. You see, he was just too full of himself to amount to any good. If you can't race a race horse, he ain't much of a race horse, right?"

The Dream Race

"Makes sense to me."

"Finally, as a last resort John Henry was gelded in an effort to calm him down enough to get him under saddle."

"What? Couldn't they just give him a stern warning. It would have worked on me."

"Well, gelding worked on John Henry and when he started winning, you can imagine what people said about him being gelded. Remember, the old saying, 'if it ain't broke don't fix it'? In this case, if John Henry hadn't been fixed he couldn't have been broke. That horse sold several times and for as low as a thousand dollars; but once he started going to work, he gathered millions in paychecks."

"Millions?"

"Over four million to be exact. Watching that black bay colt run was like watching men working on a road crew. Some horses looked like they were flying with wings. The name fit John Henry. The old folk song said John Henry swung a big hammer. So did this horse. He was a blue collar horse, but he took on all the blue bloods and never backed down. It was as if he had a score to settle, he wanted to be in the breeding barn, but it wasn't going to ever happen. So, he was going to take it out on every other horse on the track and he darn near did."

"Leonard, it sounds like you have a special place in your heart for John Henry."

"Yeah, I guess I was like millions of other people. He didn't get my respect the first time I saw him, but he earned it. Every time I saw his dark coat run past it was like magic. He looked black right until he got on top of you and then, presto, he sparkled in the sun. He glistened sky blue for a second, then blasted past and turned black again. The first time I saw it, I couldn't believe what I just saw. I turned to a groom standing next to me and asked if she saw it. She looked at me funny; so, I shut up. A minute or two later, she looked at me and said, 'You mean, the blue streak?' Oh yeah, she saw it and she couldn't believe it either. The two of us had been around horses all our lives and neither of us had ever seen a horse cast a spell as he ran by the way John Henry did. I wonder if the other horses saw it, 'cause if they did – it's no wonder they didn't want to get too close to him as he ran away from 'em."

Leonard felt the seams in the coke bottle. He closed his eyes for a moment as he slid his hands up the curved grooves in the bottle. "Eighty-three races, number eighty-four was supposed to be the first Breeders' Cup."

I pulled out my pencil and started to write down some notes. Without even opening his eyes, Leonard knew what I was writing. He recited out loud the names of the Iron Horses to help me. His eyes remained closed and his hands continued to scan the bottle.

"Roamer, Old Rosebud, Stymie, Seabiscuit, Armed, Kelso, John Henry, Cigar, Forego . . ."

I was writing as fast as I could, but then I had to stop. "Wait a minute, who's Forego?"

"Forego was another gelding with a long career at the track. It just so happens he came along at the same time as Secretariat. When a horse wins the Triple Crown for the first time after twenty-five years, all other horses are after thoughts and it's too bad. Richard Stone Reeves, the greatest equine artist of all-time for my money, said it best when he said, 'All

any one cares about any more are three year olds because of the Triple Crown. It's a shame because there are a lot of great horses who don't come into their own until after their three-year-old season. Forego was there when Secretariat won the Derby, but he was still there when horses like Seattle Slew and Affirmed won their crowns as well. Forego was the three time Horse-of-the-Year and the four time handicap Horse-of-the-Year, starting the year after Secretariat won the crown in '73. You do the math and you'll see Forego besting a whole lot of more famous horses.

"Leonard, I hear the term handicap all the time, what does it mean?"

"Well Twain, the life blood of any business is money, in racing it's the money bet on the horses. Handicapping is a way of trying to equal out the field. Specific weights are set for the horses in handicap races. One horse may carry a hundred pounds, another may carry a hundred and twenty pounds, and a third may carry a hundred and twenty-one pounds."

The Dream Race

"Just one pound difference? Like that would make a lot of difference on the back of a thousand pound horse." I was sure Leonard was setting me up for another one of his classic counter punches.

"This may not be science like in some college text book, but over hundreds of years, they know if you add one pound to a horse it adds a fraction of a second. That's all it takes to allow the other horses to gain a length at the end of the race. Handicapping isn't a science; it's an art. A third grade teacher could explain the math, but it would take a team of rocket scientists to explain the art of handicapping."

"So, what does it mean to be the handicapping Horse-of-the-Year?"

"Number one; it means the horse can carry weight. The track officials did everything they could to even up the races on Forego, everything short of throwing an anchor on his back. Forego and Kelso were two of the best weight carriers the track has ever seen. These two proved handicapping wasn't a science, because Forego and Kelso broke the laws of nature almost every time they came down the stretch with up to 140 pounds; twenty, thirty, or even forty pounds more than other horses. History says they should slow down and get caught in the stretch, their will to win said something else."

Leonard finally set the bottle back on the table. It had entertained him for long enough. He was ready to leave, he was suddenly getting ancy.

"So, who all you got in the Iron Horse Race?" Leonard asked.

"Now then, with Forego that makes . . . ten horses. Is that how many you have in the Iron Horse Race?"

Leonard took a quick look at my notes and didn't even hesitate. "No, there's one more. He's another one from about the time of Roamer and Old Rosebud. He may be the reason those two don't get talked about as much as they should; his name was Exterminator. Now, this horse set some serious records for longevity. It was his record that Stymie broke for the number of starts. Exterminator ran in a hundred races, but even more amazing is that he won fifty of them. Tell you another little known secret. Of all the old time records that have fallen over the years, Exterminator still owns the record

for the most stakes wins with thirty-three. Think about it, nearly a hundred years and no one's done it. About all of Man o' War's records have been broken from the same time period; the record standing the test of time for durability and success is Exterminator. Look at it this way, today a horse would have to race ten times every year for five years and never lose to equal Exterminator's mark, and thirty-three of those would have to be the biggest races on the planet, stakes races. They said Gehrig's record would never be broken, well I think Stymie's 133 starts and Exterminator's 33 stakes wins are going to be with us for a long time."

Leonard stood and stretched his back. "You know, they called Exterminator 'Old Bones'. Let me tell you something. I saw that horse when he was almost thirty years old. He looked like he could still get on the track and win another couple races. He ran those old bones 'til he was ten. Even though I never saw him run; I have a feelin' if Stymie had set the record before Exterminator came along, Old Bones would've kept chuggin' along. He was the original Iron Horse."

Leonard creaked out his back one more time for dramatic effect and started heading for the door. "Son, pay the lady. We've still got work to do. You think we can sit around here all day, just talkin'?"

"Sally, how much?"

"Boy, these are on the house." She leaned forward and whispered in my ear. "Leonard is one of my oldest and dearest friends. I just love to hear him talk about the Dream Race and if he likes you enough to share the story, then this one's on me."

"But . . ."

"Young man, don't argue with me. Now, get out of here. You're keeping Leonard from his chores."

"Yes Ma'am." I hit the door in the next breath and Mr. Williams got off the hook for a whole two dollars. Then again, I guess I could always buy him a win ticket for the Dream Race instead.

The Dream Race

Trinity: Blood-Horse magazine's panel of experts selected the top 100 hundred race horses of the 20th Century. Topping the poll were the magnificent three of Man o' War, Secretariat, and Citation.

Trinity

It had been a long day, at least for a kid like me who thought a couple hours of typing was a hard day's work. The whole reason to go to college was to never have to do manual labor. It wasn't about getting a good job as much as it was about avoiding getting stuck with a bad one. In school the concept was called the sweat coefficient; it was the most important thing learned during my sophomore year. It was simple enough; any job that resulted in sweating during

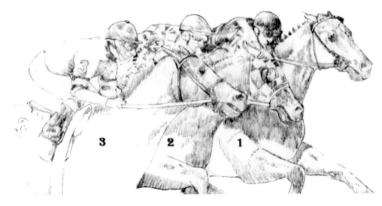

Trinity

1. Man o' War
2. Secretariat
3. Citation

working hours was unacceptable. There were a few specific exceptions, such as professional athlete; but for the most part if a job violated this one simple rule, then it was not a suitable job for a college educated person. So, here I was not only sweating through everything I was wearing, which violated all the principles that higher education stood for; but furthermore and most shocking of all, I was loving it.

The other thing I was beginning to understand was the plain and simple fact that I was learning more in a day with Leonard than I had in any class or entire semester at the university. Leonard's style was captivating. This old man had an energy, which defied his age. I could almost repeat every word he said, verbatim. Leonard was a teacher, but unlike any teacher I had ever known. I'd had very knowledgeable teachers, some of the brightest minds on the planet; but still Leonard has something none of them had.

That's when it hit me. It was his wild unbridled passion that separated him from all my academic teachers. These scholars proudly carried the banner of education, but they were missing one thing. They lacked the enthusiasm; the kind that makes you talk all day and never tire, the most convincing

131

form of propaganda known to man. Leonard's fanatical affliction was infectious and it was powerful. The Dream Race was not a story that I had to drag out of him, it was a river, a flood, it was the tide coming in; an unstoppable force of nature. And there was no reason on this planet I would ever want to stop it. The more he talked, the more I drank from the river of information. It wasn't like being drowned in the flood; it was more like surfing on the waves crashing to the shore. His enthusiasm was refreshing, nourishing, and addictive.

The day was drawing to a close. I had acted out a real life version of Tom Sawyer's painting of the fence. For most of the day I did virtually all of Leonard's chores. How ironic, here I was the nephew of Mark Twain and it was Leonard who handed me the allegorical brush and convinced me how much fun it was to paint the fence. I still wasn't ready to hand the brush back. Leonard had me paint the fence for him and I was thanking him in return.

"Long day?" Leonard not only knew his horses, it was as if he could read my mind. Then, again he probably smelled my all-day deodorant signaling the end of the day.

"Yeah and hot," I slumped back against the wall.

"It's a hot one today," Leonard said as he wiped his forehead.

"Yeah, I don't have a dry spot left on my body. "

"Speaking of hot, remember the track in Tijuana, Mexico is called Caliente? That's Spanish for hot." Leonard didn't wait for my answer, he just kept going. "But, I'll tell you where hot really is, it's Florida. Whether it was Hialeah, Tropical Park, or Gulfstream; the racing heated up in the early in the South Florida heat."

"Miami?"

"Yep, when you're talkin' hot, you're talkin' Miami. It's a place where history and beauty go hand in hand with the sport; just like the thoroughbred breed. Sadly, Hialeah closed for the last time a few years ago, but there was never a more beautiful scene than Hialeah. The backside was a tropical paradise. It had more flowering plants than a botanical garden. Man, I mean it was right out the Bible and the story of Genesis. It was the Garden of Eden and now Hialeah is gone just like Eden, but it's still the perfect setting for one of the Dream Races. You see, the horses file into a circular paddock with a giant banyan tree right in the center. Banyans grow from the

sky to the ground. The roots drop down from above and spread out as they change from roots to branches to trunks. The horses circle around this huge banyan as they wait for their riders to be put up, a dozen jockeys with silks of every color. Between Hialeah's flowers and the jockeys' silks every color of the rainbow was right before your eyes. It is the only place where I just stood and took it all in. I remember thinking, 'this must be what it's like in heaven'. It was then and there many years ago when I first imagined the Dream Races."

"Why is it closed?"

"Boy, just like the Garden of Eden, man lost the privilege to be there. Some blame it on the neighborhood; others will tell you it was politics. It doesn't make any difference, the taste of the apple was sweet and now paradise is only a memory, a beautiful memory; but a memory none the less."

"And this is where the Dream Race begins, at Hialeah?"

"You know, racing in Florida began in the early 1930s. I was there the first season. Hialeah had been privately running races for exhibition, you know, with no betting . . . well, not officially. Once betting was legalized, Hialeah was beat to the punch by Tropical Park, another track on the other side of Miami. Tropical Park stopped racing over twenty years ago as other tracks like Gulfstream and Calder squeezed the horse players by offering new, modern facilities. Maybe that's what happened to Hialeah, but it is still a mystery how a track like Hialeah with all its history and splendor could meet the same fate. I just can't imagine it." Leonard paused, kicked the ground a little bit, and spit.

"You a religious man, Twain?"

"Well, somewhat."

Leonard laughed at my answer, which gave me the false sense that he liked my answer.

"Religion isn't something you somewhat do or don't do, either you are or you aren't."

His tangled words made sense and usually when that happened, it meant he was making a net to snag me.

"Let me ask you this. Christian religion refers to the Trinity; do you know what that means?"

"The Father, the Son, and . . . and"

"And the Holy Ghost. Son, I stand corrected. With two out of three, I guess a person can be somewhat religious after all."

"Give me some credit; I could have said the 'Gray Ghost'."

"If you had, at least I would have known you'd been listening. Boy, the Trinity represents the big three. Together they comprise all that exists in the universe, heaven, and earth."

"Yeah . . . so . . ."

"Horse racing has its big three as well. They come from three different generations. The people from each of those eras could not imagine that any horse could be their equal. Each horse set all kinds of records; but what was more amazing was that they were living legends."

Leonard flipped off the lights on his way out of the barn.

"The Dream Race becomes almost impossible to take beyond this point. If the race is run one day, one horse wins; if it is run another day, another horse wins. The three horses with no equal are too close to call as they come down the backstretch."

"But, if they have no equal how ca . . . . ?"

"Good question, the answer is simple and it's a matter of opinion more than anything else. You see, I could tell you who the greatest horse of all-time is; but that answer is my answer."

"But, isn't the Dream Race, your dream race?" I asked.

"Yeah, and shouldn't you have your own dream race; for that matter, shouldn't everyone have their own dream race. It wouldn't be fair to any of these three great champions to pick one winner over the other two." Leonard said as he stared into the evening sky.

"After all this, Leonard, please don't tell me that you're going to leave me hanging with no winner in the Dream Race."

"Oh, there is definitely a winner. The question is which horse will it be. I will tell you this much for now. The winner will be one of the Trinity."

"This Trinity that you keep referring to, who is it?"

"We have been talking for a while. You've been hearing the stories of the greatest horses of all time. From what you've heard so far, who do you think the Trinity is?"

"I guess if I had to begin the list, I would start with Man o' War."

"That's interesting, why would you start there?"

"Well, as much as anything else, every time you mention his name, I get the same feeling I used to get when I was sitting in Bible school as a kid."

"Excellent, that is the perfect answer. So, who does your gut instinct tell you were the other two members of the Trinity?"

I eyed Leonard carefully. He asked his question and was prepared to wait quietly as long as needed to hear my answer. While his lips stayed motionless, his eyes scanned me as if searching for the answer somewhere on me. Somehow he knew I had the names; they were somewhere in my head and he was going to let me figure it out.

"Secretariat?"

"Are you asking me or are you telling me?"

Actually I wished he hadn't asked me that. I wasn't a hundred percent sure. He was like a dog smelling fear.

"I'm telling you: Secretariat."

"I'll buy that, but why?"

"Gut instinct? I know there has to be more to it than that, but you'll have to tell me why?"

"Well, Twain, that was another good answer." When Leonard called me Twain, it felt good. He seemed to bestow it with approval.

"Thanks, Leonard."

"Well . . .?"

"Well, I guess you want me to name the third part of the Trinity."

"Uh huh,"

"Citation," this time I answered without hesitation.

"Why?"

"I'm right aren't I?"

"Yeah, but I asked you first."

The Dream Race

All I could do was shrug my shoulders. It was a gesture I had picked up from my father. For all I know, Dad could have learned it from his father who learned it from his father who learned it from a distant uncle named Samuel to his family or Mark to the rest of the world. All I know is that in our house the shrug of the shoulders said everything without saying anything. The Clemens shrug had worked again as Leonard couldn't argue with it. He felt compelled to answer his own question.

"Yep, Man o' War, Citation, and Secretariat; not necessarily in that order. That's the Trinity of racing, the big three."

"I knew it." I had to boast a little. Out of all the horses we had talked about, I was able to name the three horses in the final cut. I had gone from complete neophyte to a blooming genius; well, at least in my own mind. That's OK, I mean at least I was able to find the metaphorical light switch and wasn't condemned to lifelong darkness. I was more impressed than Leonard was, but then again he practically spoon fed every one of the answers to me; all I had to do was stay awake in class.

"Yeah, we've talked about every one of them. I could keep yakking until I'm blue in the face about their biggest wins, the match race, their track records, their earnings . . . there are a hundred legends to go with each story and we could talk all day and only scratch the surface of each of these three's accomplishments. Then, again each of these horses could be and were beaten. What made them great was their impact on the sport and the way the public embraced each of them as something more than a horse. They were legends during their lifetimes; immortalized by the public. Their greatness is as much in their mystic as it is their speed, their pedigree, or anything else. They were torch bearers for the sport, a bright flaming torch passed from one generation to the next. Each was a blaze of glory, but together they are the most dynamic trio the sport has." Leonard stopped suddenly.

"Torch bearers, uh?"

Leonard didn't answer me. He simply turned to watch the sunset for a moment. The fiery glow lit his face with the dark umbers of shadows set off with the warm light reflecting from his profile. He closed his eyes as he stared at the last rays of the day's sun. He paused with eyes closed and stood as if he was all alone. He was quiet and I did everything I could to

disappear from his private world. As quietly as he stood, I stood even quieter. I watched the sun, the same way he did. I closed my eyes for a brief moment. When I opened them, I almost expected Leonard to be gone, either from walking away when I wasn't looking or from vanishing into a dream; perhaps the dream he was sharing with me.

Leonard was exactly the way I had left him when I'd closed my eyes. Then, again maybe I was right all along, maybe he did leave. For all practical purposes he was gone. He was at Hialeah or was it Tropical Park. It was one of those places visited only in memories. He was there watching the Big Three, the Trinity, and they were battling down the backstretch. Three horses who had run away from the rest of the world were now locked together in Leonard's mind. They were running as one; three hearts beating as one and a dozen legs pounding like the pistons of one incredible powerful machine.

His eyes opened and he turned to look at me.

"You were there, weren't you?" I asked.

"Where?" Leonard replied to see if I knew what I was asking or just taking a lucky swing for the fence.

"The Dream Race."

"Yeah, boy, that's right."

"Hialeah?" I asked.

"How's that?"

"Hialeah . . . by any chance were you at Hialeah?"

This time I think I really did startle Leonard.

"Yeah, but how did you know that?"

"Well, it was just a hunch."

"Writer's instinct?" Leonard looked at me and winked. He was right and for the first time, I knew what writer's instinct was.

"Yeah, maybe . . . so I was right, you were at the Dream Race at Hialeah . . . and you were watching the Trinity."

"Boy, I can tell you a thousand times what Hialeah looked like and you'll never get it. So, let's try this . . . look over there at the last cloud that's still all lit up. See how it looks like it's burning on the inside."

"Yes, I see it."

The Dream Race

"Keep your eyes fixed on that one cloud, that one burning cloud. Beautiful, isn't it?"

"Uh huh."

"Imagine that you have never seen a sunset before. Now, really look at that cloud . . . see all the colors, see the way the colors are glowing. Isn't it the most beautiful thing you have ever seen?"

"Yeah," I have to admit, he was right. What had I been missing all my life?

"Now, multiply that by a thousand times in its beauty. Is it getting more beautiful, more intense?"

"Yes."

"Close your eyes." I did as he said. "Now, let that cloud become the three horses, the Trinity. Your eyes have never seen anything more beautiful. You see them moving together as one. They're not racing against each other, they are running together; working together the way a crew does with their oars. They reach out into the water and pull the boat underneath them. The Trinity pulls the ground under them the same way; together they skim across the ground, cruising faster than any one horse could go alone."

I waited for Leonard to tell me more, to put more pictures in my mind; but he left me in silence – I was alone with Man o' War, Citation, and Secretariat. There was no crowd, no cheering. It was a serene quiet. Then I began to hear a distant rumble. The rumble turned to thunder. The thunder of their hooves splashing past me was deafening. I watched them streak past me like a clipper with a full bellied sail. Behind them was the lake in the track's infield adding to the visual analogy of the horses gliding across the water. The crew was pulling together. Hooves pounding, oars reaching, and engines roaring; all translate into speed. Their precise movements were a constant pulsing, pistons pumping, and hitting on all cylinders . . . stroke . . . stroke . . . stroke . . . the three flew over the ground and sailed over the water behind them. In this group they ran as one. There wasn't a win, a place, or a show. It was all show! It was the greatest show that any one could ever imagine. It wasn't the greatest show on Earth; no, no, this was from some other place, a place called heaven.

It was the Dream Race and for the first time, Leonard didn't have to say a word. I was seeing it for myself. Man o' War, Citation, and Secretariat each was the greatest horse of

all-time to a different generation. Their legions were passionate, vocal, and emphatic that each was in their day the best. To expect any one who saw Secretariat to believe that a better horse ever lived would be impossible to believe. Those who cheered for Man o' War would never have imagined another of his stature would ever come along. Yet, in heaven they run together.

"Yes, torch bearers" Leonard finally answered when his eyes opened after a couple minutes; just long enough for him to watch a mile and a fraction scorched in record time.

It was all right there for my eyes to see. It was all right there in that burning cloud. Each of the Trinity were torch bearers for a sport that has been passed from generation to generation. It was all right there in Leonard's story about the Dream Race. Now, yes now, I knew I could write the article Mr. Williams had asked for. There wasn't just one greatest horse of all-time. There's over three hundred years of champions; dynasties built from royal pedigrees, and freaks of nature whose speed can't be explained in any other way except that it was sent from heaven.

The Fourth Crown: What if the eleven Triple Crown winners could be placed on the track at one time, who would win? Where would they race? What would it be called? The answer to the second question is Saratoga. The answer to the last question is the Fourth Crown. The first question is a matter to be debated.

The Fourth Crown

The day's work was done; even if it took us into part of the night to get it that way. I still didn't have a clear cut answer to the question of who was the greatest horse of all-time; somehow it didn't seem to matter. That was the biggest lesson I had learned from Leonard. The answer wasn't any one

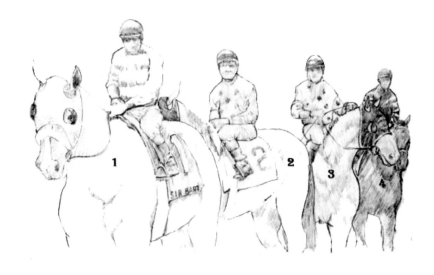

Fourth Crown

1. Sir Barton
2. Gallant Fox
3. Omaha
4. War Admiral

horse. It wasn't that simple. There were too many factors. The weather, the track, you name it; the answer to the question and the outcome to any of the Dream Races would be subject to a wide range of variables. Was it on turf, where was it run, what distance and maybe many more details could influence the outcome. The answer to the question was becoming less important than the history of the breed. The mountain of stories surrounding the cast of characters, and the hallowed ground these races were run on became the focus. Leonard had made it simple; he just said the Dream Race was heaven. The more he talked during the course of the day the more I realized what he meant by heaven.

I watched Leonard head off to his old truck after our last goodbyes of the day. Tomorrow I was going to be back at the newspaper, and the Dream Race would again be relegated to the privacy of Leonard's mind. There it would remain his secret, until the next lucky soul gets invited to spend a day with Leonard at heaven's track to experience the Dream Race. Leonard looked back while opening the door of his truck.

"Hey, Scoop, don't you need a ride back to your car?"

The Dream Race

"I'd totally forgotten about it." And I really had totally forgotten about my sole means of escape. Maybe this day wasn't so bad after all.

"Let's go, I've got to be back here in a few hours."

Leonard was right. It was just enough time to eat and sleep before coming back and doing it all over again; but the funny thing was Leonard didn't seem to mind. Matter of fact, it seemed as if he couldn't wait to get back.

"Lucky you."

"That's right. Lucky me." Leonard smiled as I jumped in the other side. "Luck, the kind of luck it would take to win the fourth crown."

"The fourth crown? OK, Leonard, you got me. What's the fourth crown?"

"Well, when talking about the Dream Races, it's one of the last races I want to talk about."

"Why's that?"

"Simple, it's because whenever someone thinks about the greatest horse of all-time or hears about the Dream Race, they always think this is the answer to the question." Leonard eased out of the farm at the same methodical pace he delivered his stories.

"Could you explain that?"

"Yeah, just about everyone who knows a little about horses would think the greatest horse of all-time has to be a Triple Crown winner and that could be true, but not necessarily."

"I think I know what you mean . . . like Man o' War or . . . or Native Dancer . . .or"

"Twain, you're right as rain. You've been listening, haven't you?"

I shrugged. Modesty was a new quality for me; one which I hadn't mastered, yet. I had a feeling if I spent more time with Leonard I could get the hang of it. It was the way he personified his cool.

"Or it could be Eclipse or Kelso or Spectacular Bid or Ruffian . . . it all depends, it just all depends." Leonard added.

"So, the Fourth Crown is . . ." I waited for Leonard to fill in the blank for me.

"The Dream Race for the Fourth Crown features eleven horses; yeah, those eleven, the eleven winners of the Triple Crown: starting with Sir Barton in 1919, then continuing with Gallant Fox in '30, Omaha in '35, War Admiral, Whirlaway, Count Fleet, Assault, Citation, Secretariat . . ."

"Seattle Slew in '77 and Affirmed in '78," I finished the list to show off a bit.

"Yeah, that's right. You have been doing your homework."

"It's easy when you've got a good teacher." I figured a little blatant flattery couldn't hurt. Plus, it was true; this old man made his Dream Race story my easiest history lesson. Leonard ignored my feeble attempt to stroke his ego and continued with the story.

"You see, these horses have all attained their place in history. No matter what else happens, they are now legends."

"Why is it, I always get a feeling you don't like some of these Triple Crown winners?"

"Son, it ain't that I don't like 'em. I just don't think these eleven are automatically the best horses of all-time.

Now, with that being said, they all earned their fame and I'd be the last person to take that away from any one of 'em. OK?"

"OK"

"For example, Sir Barton may be more famous today than he was in his hey day. Imagine this, his owner, John Madden didn't even consider Sir Barton his best horse. Mr. Madden was a professional horseman and breeding was the just the first step in making a winning horse. In his day, no one made more winners than Mr. Madden and he said the best he ever bred was Grey Lag. You see, Sir Barton didn't start winning until his win at the Derby."

"I guess he picked a good time to get hot."

"Son, you can say that again. Sir Barton was the first Triple Crown winner, but the match race with Man o' War probably did more for his reputation than his wins in those three now infamous races; the Derby, the Preakness, and the Belmont Stakes."

"You mean he beat Man o' War?"

"No, boy, don't be silly; but at the time to even be considered in the same class to get a head to head race with Big Red was pretty darn good to be mentioned as the second best

143

horse in the country. When the two faced off, Man o' War took the older horse to the woodshed for a good spankin'. You gotta keep in mind when Sir Barton won the Belmont to close out the first Triple Crown, there was no fanfare; no more than any other major stakes race. Sir Barton had lost a handful of races before he won the Kentucky Derby. What if I told you Sir Barton wasn't even Mr. Madden's second best horse? That's right; he also bred a horse named Zev who earned over $300,000 in the '20s. That was a ton of money back then and far and away a record. So, you see today every one can read about and tell you Sir Barton was the first Triple Crown winner, every one except John Madden who bred him; he died before the term stuck making Sir Barton the first horse to win all three races. It would be another ten years before another horse consolidated these three races again; then a reporter dubbed the feat as the Triple Crown. Yeah, that would have been 1930 when Gallant Fox did it. Let me ask you a question. Aside from all the sports writers, present company excluded, of course."

"Of course" I wasn't sure, if he had just complimented me or given the proverbial locker-room-towel-pop on the backside.

"Who do you think knows more about horses; the people who watch 'em or the people who ride them?"

"The people who ride them . . ." My answer may not have been the most confident.

"Exactly, so what do you think it would take to bring one of the greatest jockeys of all time out of retirement?" Leonard's questions were beginning to be lay-ups.

"I guess it would have to be a great horse, one the jockey knew he could win on."

"That's right and Gallant Fox was just such a horse and that's exactly what happened. Earl Sande who was already a legend had just hung up his boots, when he first saw Gallant Fox. It didn't take a lot of talkin' to get him unretired. As I've heard it, Sande did the talking. This was a horse he could finish his career on and go out in style. Everyone knew Earl Sande could win on a mule, but by 1930 Mr. Sande didn't have to ride mules; by then, it was nothing but Cadillacs for Mr. Sande. Maybe he wasn't ridin' any mules, but he did make an exception for a fox. Yeah, Gallant Fox would be his last Cadillac. Little did he know, that fox would make him more famous in the long run than all of his other horses combined.

That's right, Gallant Fox put Sande on the most prized list in all horse racing. That's what the Triple Crown has come to mean." Leonard pulled his ball cap forward and rubbed the bald top of his head and repeated himself. "The most prized list in horse racing; yes, sir, that's right."

"Gallant Fox ran for one of racing's dynasties. He ran for Mr. Woodward's Belair Stud, a racing dynasty of the era. Sometimes it's hard to say if a horse makes a farm or the other way around. Gallant Fox is the only Triple Crown winner to sire another. Gallant Fox was a good horse and his claim to greatness was reaffirmed by his son, Omaha, the third Triple Crown winner. Like his father he also raced in the Belair silks with the red and white polka dots and they both wore the red blinkers. Along with those polka dot silks came maybe the best horse trainer ever, Mr. Fitzsimmons; he was known to 'bout everyone as Mr. Fitz. I remember him as a bent over man. His back nearly crippling him, but it didn't hold him back from getting the most out of a horse. He'd just lean back, stare 'em in the eye, and they knew what they were supposed to do. If there ever was a man who could talk to horses, Mr. Fitz was it. He was the original Dr. Doolittle."

"It sure sounds like a winning combination; great horses, the best jockey, and the best trainer." I said.

"True, true, honestly though Omaha never showed himself on the track over the long-haul. He won all three races of the Triple Crown, but he didn't put fear in the hearts of his competition the way other horses have; nor was he able to pass along the talent given to him by his father." Leonard stopped mid-sentence and asked. "What do you think about when I say Omaha?"

"Well, the only thing I can think of is Nebraska."

"Right. Did you know there is a race track in Omaha? The name of the track is Aksarben; that's Nebraska spelt backwards? The folks in Nebraska took the Triple Crown winner to heart. Yeah, they did. Omaha is buried at Aksarben."

I shrugged; it's obviously one of those pieces of information that you don't have a pre-packaged answer for.

"Let me see, that brings us to the fourth Triple Crown winner. That would be War Admiral." Leonard said. "He might have been the first truly great horse to have won the Triple Crown. He looked unbeatable like his daddy, Man o'

The Dream Race

War; that was before his match race with Seabiscuit. That big black stallion was on a par with Pegasus, until he was exposed as being merely mortal after losing what may have been the most anticipated race ever. Either way you look at it; the race between War Admiral and Seabiscuit was another star in the crown of Man o' War; even if it wasn't a Triple Crown."

"There you go again, dissing the Triple Crown winners."

"Dissing?"

"Yeah, that's the lingo. You're dissing, disrespecting the Triple Crown winners when you say stuff like that." I said.

"It's no disrespect that much you can be sure of. It just may be a tip of the cap to their pappy, but believe me, it ain't disrespect. You see War Admiral was the wonder horse and beat all comers, until the match race at Pimlico. If it hadn't been for that one race, we would be talking about War Admiral with the same reverence as we do for the Trinity of Man o' War, Citation, and Secretariat. Those black and gold silks of Mr. Riddle could have easily been right there with Belair's two Triple Crown winners." Leonard said.

"So, Belair is the only farm to produce two Triple Crown winners."

"Not so fast young man; you're forgetting about Calumet Farm. The fifth Triple Crown winner was Whirlaway from Calumet who produced a lot of great horses. Whirlaway is almost forgotten at the track. When someone talks about great horses from Calumet, the horse everyone thinks of is Citation and not Whirlaway. Once his secret code was broken, Whirlaway was an unbeatable champion."

"Secret code? What secret code? You make it sound like a spy novel."

"Whirlaway was a little . . . OK, a lot spooky when it came to his track behavior. He was an uncontrollable beast at first. Then, young Jones came up with the idea to use blinkers. The genius was being able to realize blinkers weren't the whole solution because not everything was a distraction. The distraction was a screaming crowd. Whirlaway would run all over the track. It took maybe the best jockey of all time in Eddie Arcarro just to keep the beast from jumping into the grandstand. Jones cut out the right eye of Whirlaway's blinkers so he could see the track and the rail, but not see the grandstand. It was like magic. Whirlaway started winning and

he was for all practical purposes untouchable and the legend of Mr. Longtail was born." Leonard paused with that far away look he would get when he was going back in his memory to call up an image from days gone by.

"Mr. Longtail?"

"Oh, yeah. Whirlaway's trademark was this long, thick flowing tail; the kind you'd see a show horse dragging behind 'em. They didn't tie it up like on some horses. Instead, they just let it brush the top of the ground and when Mr. Longtail took off it was like the flag in front of a cavalry charge. That horse knew what he was doing as he waved it in everybody's face on his way to victory."

"OK Leonard, that makes five Triple Crown winners, who's next?"

"Count Fleet"

"Count Fleet, now there's one I hadn't heard of."

"Doesn't surprise me, he may be the most underrated of the group. This was a great horse on the track and a good stallion. Boy, you ever heard of Hertz?"

"The rental car company?"

"The same, well John Hertz was a taxi tycoon long before Hertz was number one in rental cars. He owned Count Fleet. If it helps just think of a fleet of cars and you can't help but remember that Hertz owned Count Fleet." Leonard seemed pleased sharing his little memory trick. "Count Fleet was a mean little horse. He was ridden by Johnny Longden. Longden may not have been as flamboyant as Arcarro, but his career lasted longer and he set the bar for those who would follow. Often, when a horse is as mean as Count Fleet was it means being gelded. Fortunately, it didn't come to that. Count Fleet was the leading sire several times starting with his first crop and continued for nearly thirty years; but, what we're really talkin' about is a race horse. Yes sir, a horse that liked to run; a horse that loved to win, a real competitor. As a two year old he was hard to beat; with a little extra schooling on his starts, Count Fleet was never beat again. He was undefeated through his three year old campaign, which of course included the three classics."

"Of course."

"In my opinion when you talk about the greatest of all-time Count Fleet is probably the horse that gets talked about the least who deserves to be talked about more." Hey, at this point Leonard's opinion was the gospel of horse racing as far as I was concerned. If he believed it, it was good enough for me.

"So, Twain, where does that bring us?" Leonard asked.

"Number seven, lucky number seven"

"Yeah, lucky number seven. You don't know how right you are." Leonard turned to glance at me. He waited a little longer than usual before continuing. "Assault was the seventh Triple Crown winner. He may not have been the best, but he was certainly the luckiest and I mean that with all due respect."

"Lucky on the track."

"Lucky to ever make it to the track. You see, Assault had an accident as a yearling. A spike pierced his hoof. It was nearly a fatal injury as the decision had to be made whether or not to put him down. The colt was saved, but he was left with a clubbed foot and a severe limp for the rest of his life. It was so bad that Assault actually fell down being led to the track, but he got up and ran and won. That's the stuff that makes a legend out of a horse. He may have had a bad foot, but he had a big heart and that's what America came to love in the champion they affectionately called the Clubfooted Comet."

"Clubfooted Comet? It doesn't sound all that affectionate. It sounds more like the way school children would taunt someone."

"Keep in mind, this was right after the end of World War II. A horse with this kind of never-say-die attitude was something all of America could relate to. Assault wore the 'running W' silks of the King Ranch in Texas. It was the same 'running W' branded on about 25,000 head cattle. Assault's exploits were like a John Wayne movie. He was a hero in a time when we needed all the heroes we could get. No matter how bad things were stacked against you; Assault made you believe you should never give up. Trust me, the odds were against this wounded warrior. When he started racing the odds reflected it. He was 71 to 1 when he won his first major stakes race. Who would have ever thought such a horse would end up being 'lucky number seven' on the most prized list of champions. He was the four-legged version of the old rallying cry, 'Remember the Alamo'. Assault became synonymous with never giving up. His inspiration may have been more important than his number of wins or the money he won."

"That's amazing."

"True, in this world where we are always looking for feel-good stories of inspiration, all we have to do is look back. If you thought Seabiscuit was an inspirational story, imagine the story of Assault. There's a movie I'd stand in line to see."

"Leonard, I'll buy the popcorn. Let's go!"

"They have to make the movie first."

"Leonard, write the script and they will come. Seriously, write the script."

"That's your job, Twain; not mine."

I looked up just in time to see us going past the restaurant where my car had been abandoned since breakfast. "Hey, weren't we supposed to turn in?" I asked.

"What do you want; your car or to hear about the Fourth Crown?"

"Keep driving." I replied.

"I thought so." It was dark out, but from the greenish glow from his dashboard lights, I could see the sides of his lips curl into his familiar little smile. "How about a simple question; do you know, the home of each leg of the Triple Crown?"

"I know that one; Churchill Downs for the Derby, Pimlico for the Preakness, and the Belmont Stakes."

"Very good, but can you tell me the home of the Fourth Crown?"

"Let's see. It would have run after the Belmont," I deduced out loud.

"Right . . ."

"It would have to be a monumental stage, maybe the next most important stakes race after the Belmont."

"That a boy, you're on the right track."

"It should be someplace with history and tradition; someplace revered by the racing public." I wasn't so much talking as I was thinking with my mouth.

"You're in the homestretch, son. Bring it on home."

"Saratoga. That's my guess, Saratoga."

"You need to go to the winner's circle and get your picture taken."

The Dream Race

I have to admit, I felt pretty good. When I first met Leonard I knew nothing about racing or its history. To come up with this answer felt like being named valedictorian. Leonard may have been surprised, but I could tell he was also pleased.

"Leonard, tell me more about Saratoga. I only know what you've told me, but whenever you talk about Saratoga I feel as if you are talking about holy ground." Leonard laughed before answering.

"Can't help but laugh at the thought of a racetrack as a religious site."

"Well, you are the one who said the Dream Race was in heaven."

"Touche, young man, I think every real horse racing disciple has to make the pilgrimage to Saratoga. Some might call it the birth place of racing in this country. Like I said, there were other tracks before Saratoga; but for the sake of this discussion, Saratoga is Jerusalem and Mecca rolled into one." Leonard said.

"Saratoga is not the oldest, right?"

"Well, that's not totally correct either."

"Leonard, you want to make up your mind?"

"Son, the South was the original cradle of racing in this country. New Orleans still hosts the oldest track and there were other areas in South Carolina filled with racing. The Civil War changed the hierarchy of a lot of things in this country and horse racing was one of them. The best way to see it would be to imagine horse racing like NASCAR."

"NASCAR? Hey, you're using my analogy.'

"That's right! I'm just going to take it a step farther. For many years the South's been synonymous with race cars. It was a southern, good ole boy sport. It's changin' now and the whole country is watching. That's kind of how horse racing spread out. I imagine if the automobile had never come along that horse racing would still be the most watched sport in the country. All the NASCAR fans would be at the horse track."

"OK, so we've got Jerusalem, the Civil War and the invention of the automobile all worked into this conversation and you still haven't told me anything about Saratoga."

"Just had to set up the parameters, now let's talk horses."

"Start with Saratoga."

"The first thing is to get a picture of Saratoga in your mind. Like so many tracks the architecture of the building is its calling card. You see the turrets of the roof line of the grandstand and you know it's Saratoga. The twin spires of Churchill Downs is its trademark. The pyramid shaped cupolas of Saratoga are just as well known by those who migrate to upstate New York for summer racing. The grandstand at Saratoga was the first modern sports arena in this country with its old world charm embracing the dawn of the modern era. The club house isn't air conditioned. It doesn't even have windows. The air carries the dust, the sounds of the track, and even the smell of horses into the crowd."

"Gee, I'm not too sure how appealing the last part of that sounds." I interrupted.

"You, my man, are not a horse man; not yet anyhow. If you were, you would love it. It hasn't been that long ago, Saratoga horses on their way to the track walked right through the middle of the outdoor café. If you thought the smell of horses in the grandstand was strange, then imagine it over your morning coffee; some would tell you it was the greatest smell in heaven."

"Yeah, if you say so."

"The smell of freshly oiled tack and toast, boy, you don't know what you've been missing." Leonard's laugh was never more amusing. I knew he was laughing at me, but it carried with it an approving tone.

"After Assault, you know the last four Triple Crown winners, right?" Leonard seemed to be rushing to the end of the story. That wasn't like him.

"Yeah, Citation, Secretariat, Seattle Slew, and Affirmed."

"That's an A plus." At that moment Leonard turned the truck off the road. To call it a side road was generous. In the dark I wasn't sure if it was marked or not.

"Where are we going?"

"Some place where you can get a better feel for the Fourth Crown."

We continued around a winding road. It emptied out into an open area. There was just enough light from the rising moon to make out an opening in the trees. The headlights reflected off a white fence, if you want to call it that. It was just the top rail of fence. It was a race track. I couldn't see much in the darkness in front of us. I got the feeling there wasn't a grandstand, but I couldn't see the other side of the track to get a sense of how big the track was. Leonard stopped a few feet from the fence and was out of the truck before I could ask another question. I shook my head and followed. Leonard leaned against the rail. I did the same. I had no sooner assumed the position next to him, than he scurried back to the truck and turned off the lights, leaving me in the dark and this time it was more than a metaphor.

"Can you see 'em?" Leonard called out.

"See 'em; see who?" I was sure Leonard had lapsed into senility.

"The eleven entries."

"What?"

"The horses running for the Fourth Crown; the eleven Triple Crown winners. Do you see 'em?"

"I can't see anything. If you haven't noticed, it's a little dark out here."

"How else do you expect to see 'em? Look out there, listen . . . listen . . . way out there on the other side of the track. Listen to them coming this way. Hear 'em?"

"No, I don . . ."

"Shhhhh, you gotta listen."

"But, you said . . ."

"Shhhh . . .shhh . . . here they come."

I waited quietly not sure if Leonard had totally lost it. In the silence I suspended my disbelief. I allowed the darkness of the track to become the void of my own imagination. It was like closing my eyes and dreaming, but with my eyes open and ears alert. The more I waited the more I really began to believe. My doubts turned into anticipation.

The ground seemed to rumble underneath me. I touched the rail in front of me. I swear I could feel it shake. I strained my eyes in an effort to peer into the darkness. I couldn't see anything, but as the ground began to pound harder I was sure I heard the roar of a stampede coming my way. I glanced at Leonard. He was beside me, but I couldn't see his face. My head whirled back around. In the distance, in the blackness I could make out the silhouette of shadows bounding toward me or was it the trees on the other side of the track starting to show as my eyes adjusted to the night? The roar grew louder sounding like a distant tornado.

"Close your eyes," Leonard's voice was just loud enough to be heard over the storm. I blinked, but I couldn't keep them closed as I wanted to see what was coming. Curiosity was growing as fast as the noise was building. I forced my eyes closed again. Despite all temptation to do otherwise, I kept them closed, squeezed tightly shut.

"Keep 'em closed." I followed Leonard's directions as I fought the instinct to peek. Call it a reporter's professional curiosity or human instinct; either way something inside me was begging me to open my eyes. Some how, some way, I was able to keep them closed and focus my sight into my imagination as the rumbling raced toward me.

"Do you see 'em?"

My eyes were closed; it was a stupid question. Just as I started to tell Leonard as such; I SAW THEM! They were bounding at me in a tight pack that swelled to fill the entire track. There was not a step between any of them. They were banging into one another. The dirt flying up between them looked like smoke from their blistering hooves. I began to count. One, two, three; it was almost impossible to keep track as they jockeyed for position. Four, five, six of them; digging their way straight at me. Seven, eight, nine, ten, eleven horses

moving like a massive locomotive. I kept my eyes closed as they raced toward me. The roar was thunderous. Through the noise I could hear Leonard's voice in the role of the track announcer.

"And here they come . . ."

I saw them as clearly in my mind as if I was standing at the rail at Saratoga watching them charge toward me. My imagination had taken over the details of the race. The Fourth Crown was about to be settled and it was going to happen right here in front of me and hundred thousand other people conjured up in the roar of the horses hooves. In the pitch black of night, I was lost in the sunlight of Saratoga. I could see dirt being slung ten, fifteen feet into air. The horses closed in on me and the noise mounted. I started to make out their silks. Instead of just being a pack of one, the individual horses began to emerge. I saw up front the blue and white checks of Secretariat, followed closely behind by several red shirts. There was one, two, three; actually I'm not sure how many red shirts were right on the heels of the big red chestnut in the blue and white. Two almost black horses looked even more ominous with their black silks trimmed in gold, Slew and War Admiral. Along side the charcoal and pink of Affirmed, the group was bunched, but now even the jockeys' faces were getting clearer. There was Arcaro on Citation; even at a distance, I could see the nose which earned him the nickname 'Banana Nose'. I could see the cool face of Torcott out in front. He peeked under his arm to view the field behind him.

Behind them I saw the polka-dotted silks of the Belair horses. Omaha may have been in over his head and his sire wasn't leaving him too far behind. At the back of the group was the Assault. I remembered his injured hoof and how they thought he would never run. I couldn't help but think of him as the heavy underdog and ultimate champion just by being a part of this illustrious field. I could see his eyes focused on the horses right in front of him. There was no quit in this horse and as long as the race wasn't over, it wasn't over for him. If he didn't count himself out, who was I to do the same.

Speaking of counting, there was a sudden blur from the pack and with that blink of the eye Citation and Secretariat had company at the front. It was Count Fleet and he was gaining. Count Fleet knew why he was there and he was going to make a game of it.

"And down the stretch they come . . ." Leonard's voice strained to break through the rumble drowning my ears. The noise nearly washed the words from his voice.

I checked to the right to see how far the horses were from the finish line and quickly looked back. There was plenty of room for any number of horses to still capture the Fourth Crown; it was a matter of who wanted it the most and with that being the case I started pulling for Assault to make a Herculean move from the back. I had stayed neutral through all of Leonard's stories all day long, now I couldn't help but want this gutsy, little horse to pull off one more miracle.

"Come on!" I called out loud.

At that moment I heard a train's horn blow. The sound snapped my trance. My eyes popped open. I realized the roar wasn't just noise coming from within my head, but it was real. Leonard had brought me to a track that was just a few hundred yards from a railroad track.

"Boy, you were really there, weren't you?" Leonard asked with a bit of curiosity.

I wasn't sure if I should be mad at him for pulling such a trick on me or not; but really, how could I be mad? I was actually glad to have experienced the race even if it was a trick.

"How did you know?" I asked.

"Know that you would see them?"

"Yeah, how did you know I would see them?"

"Son, the train may have been real, but that doesn't mean the horses weren't real in their own way."

"OK, so why didn't you let me watch until the race was over?"

"I'm not sure it would have answered your question about who was the greatest of all time. If you thought that train was a horse race, there's no telling what you would have believed, if you saw the finish line." Even in the dark I could see Leonard wink at me. "So, who were you yelling for when you opened your eyes?"

I was reluctant to answer; but this was Leonard's Dream Race, the least I could do is tell what I saw for that brief moment when I stood in heaven watching the race for the Fourth Crown.

"Assault, but I'm not sure why."

Leonard nodded. It was as if he knew my answer and was only asking to make sure. "The race is over, let's call it a day and head home." Leonard paused before adding his own personal segue. "Heading home at the end of the day, that reminds me of the last race on the Dream Race card. I'll tell you about it in the truck." With that said, Leonard left me standing in the dark; which is somehow appropriate since all of his stories somehow left me in the dark groping for more.

The Dream Race

All Good Things: Calumet Farm became the prototype of success in all sports, not just horse racing. Their dynasty produced more stakes winners, eight Hall-of-Fame horses, two Hall-of-Fame trainers, two Triple Crown winners, and five Horse-of-the-Year honors; produced the first horse to earn a half-million dollars as well as the first horse to earn a million dollars, and dominated the owners' list for nearly two decades.

All good things ….

We were back in Leonard's old truck. My ears were still ringing after the train's horn practically knocked me down minutes earlier. Leonard rolled his truck back onto a paved road after his little side trip to the old abandoned track. It had to be nearly midnight and I knew one of us had to get up pretty early the next day to repeat the day's events. It wasn't me I was worried about. I guess Leonard knew how to live on a couple hours sleep. I was feeling pretty good thinking about

All Good Things…

1. Whirlaway & Jimmy Jones
2. Twilight Tear & Ben Jones
3. Armed
4. Citation

the fact that I didn't have to get up until seven. No amount of coffee could get me out of bed at four every day. Then again, apparently it wasn't the coffee that got Leonard going in the morning. It was the horses.

"All good things must come to an end." It was another of Leonard's comments from out of the blue, but with a purpose. The reason may not be clear at the moment; but as with all of his stories, Leonard was going somewhere with it.

"Yeah, I have to admit I really enjoyed shoveling horse manure all day." I said half seriously and half tongue-in-cheek. I guess when discussing horse manure, there has to be a better reference than 'tongue-in-cheek'.

"That was just a bonus."

"Yeah, I know, the real treat was hanging out with you all day." I was chiding him. He knew it, and he liked it.

"Lucky you."

"You're right, Leonard, all good things must come to an end."

"You do know I wasn't referring to today. I was referring to the last race of the day at the Dream Race."

The Dream Race

"And this is the final Dream Race?"

"Yeah, you see, when you go to the races, the big race is never the last race. They always follow it with another race. It's like the epilogue at the end of a book."

"An epilogue, huh?"

"That's right."

"And this race is called, 'All good things must come to an end'?"

"That name would work as well as a few others. I guess I haven't got a name for this race."

"Well, what can you tell me about this one."

"Son, right off the bat, I can tell you it's a race announcer's nightmare." Leonard chuckled at his little secret.

"What makes it a nightmare, is it scary?"

"No, no, no, it's not a scary nightmare; it's more like a headache nightmare. You see, all the jockeys are wearing the same silks."

"What? Why?"

"OK, we've been at this all day. So, tell me what you know about silks."

"Well, each farm has their own colors and pattern."

"Then, if every horse carried the same silks, what would that mean?" Leonard continued to question me in an effort to lead me to the answer.

"I guess every horse in the race runs for the same farm."

"That's right."

"Leonard, are you telling me that one farm has enough horses to fill a race to determine the greatest horse of all time?"

"It's something like that."

"Do you mind explaining that?" I asked.

"Well, while no one farm has a monopoly on greatness, there's been a few farms consistently sending stakes winner after stakes winner to the track; some over a period of a few years. However, this Dream Race would feature horses from over five decades; that's right, for fifty years one farm was a threat to send a Triple Crown winner to the track on any given year."

All good things ....

"Did they ever get one?"

"Twice" Leonard took his eyes off the dark road to see if I could put the pieces together.

"Twice, uh?"

"Yeah, so . . ."

"So, that means this Dream Race would either be Belair Stud or Calumet. Belair had Gallant Fox and Omaha; and Calumet had Whirlaway and Citation."

"You're right, but before I ask you which one, I have to ask you another question. What do three of those Triple Crown winners have in common?"

Just when I thought I was about to finish Leonard's game of twenty questions, he changed the game. "I thought you were going to ask me which farm. I have no idea what those horses have in common; four legs?"

"Boy, you're too easily flustered."

"Tired, not flustered," I said.

"Ya sound flustered, if you're asking me. OK, since you're not even going to take a stab at it. It's Teddy."

"Teddy? Who's Teddy, a trainer, a breeder, or a big cuddly bear?"

"No, no, no . . . Teddy's a stallion and maybe one of the best stallions of his day. He's Gallant Fox's sire line . . ."

"Which means he's Omaha's as well." I wasn't going to let the old man have all the glory.

"Very good."

"And how does Teddy tie into one of the others?" I asked.

"Teddy is Bull Lea's sire line and that makes him Citation's; just like Gallant Fox and Omaha. Not a lot of horses have three Triple Crown winners that close in their get."

"So, is Teddy in the final Dream Race?"

"No, but let me go back to the original question; whose silks are all the jockeys wearing?" Leonard asked.

"Well, between Belair and Calumet; my guess would be Calumet."

Leonard seemed pleased with my answer. "What makes you say that?"

159

The Dream Race

"Well, in addition to the two Triple Crown winners, you said they were around for fifty years. Belair wasn't around that long and I know I've heard you mention a Calumet horse in almost everyone of the Dream Races. Matter of fact about the only American Dream Race without a Calumet horse was the Dream Distaff. Calumet didn't have a filly in the race." My remark made Leonard laugh, but it was a different laugh.

"There could have very well been a few in the Dream Distaff. The first filly ever to be Horse-of-the-Year was a Calumet product, Twilight Tear. That's right, I'll tell you something else; the filly, Bewitch, was the last horse to beat Citation before he started his sixteen race win streak. Think about this; sixteen straight wins still shares the record to this day over fifty years later. Now, image this; if Bewitch hadn't stopped Citation, the win streak would have been twenty-nine races. Now, like I've said before, someday some horse is going to beat sixteen; twenty-nine is a number that would be harder to beat than Joe Dimaggio's 56 game hitting streak; that's a record some say may be the most difficult to break in all of sports. I assure you, twenty-nine would be a record that would last forever. Now, think about this then when you think about how good Twilight Tear and Bewitch were."

"Bewitch, the horse who cast a spell on Citation." I said.

"A bit melodramatic, don't you think."

"Maybe a bit"

"Actually, the loss really shows the greatness of Calumet."

"How do you mean, Leonard?"

"Well, Calumet had three horses in the race and frankly Mr. Wright thought they could finish one, two, three. So, he instructed the jockeys not to burn up the horses, if it was one of the three Calumet horses was in front. As he predicted, the Calumet horses finished one, two, three. The master, Eddie Arcaro, was on Citation who came in second. He said after the race Citation had plenty to run down any horse on the track. Oh, yeah, Bewitch was good, but twenty-nine in a row was a streak no one would have ever touched. If Mr. Wright or the Joneses had any idea of the historical significance of that race, maybe the instructions would have been a little different."

"The Joneses are . . ."

"Mr. Ben and his son, Jimmy; they took Calumet from a farm with a lot of money invested in the horse business to a

farm that won more races than any other farm in the business. Boy, sometimes you should take a minute to go see the Calumet trophy collection. They have some five-hundred trophies taking up a whole room. After Mr. Wright's widow, Mrs. Markey passed away the farm was sold and the people around Lexington felt so strongly about what Calumet meant to racing that they pitched in about a million dollars to keep the collection together. Son, that is respect; the kind no one horse can get you. I'm talking about a dynasty that was built on great horses, sound breeding, and lots of know-how from the best people. The Joneses were the final ingredient in making the sweetest cake ever baked by Calumet. Sweetest cake, do ya get it?"

"Not really, should I?"

"You will, Allen." I almost fainted; Leonard had never called me by my real first name before. "When Ben Jones first worked with Whirlaway, he was a horse with plenty of speed to burn and that's just what he did. The problem was that he burnt it from side to side as much as he did going forward. He went everywhere except backwards and in horse racing, if you aren't going straight ahead then you might as well be going backwards. Truth is, it was little Jimmy who came up with the brilliant idea to put the one-eyed blinkers on Whirlaway that I told you about. Well, the next thing you know the horse is running straight as an arrow and faster than a bullet."

"You're telling me, that Whirlaway would have never won a race if they hadn't covered one eye."

"He had the speed to win, but not the direction to be considered among the greats of all-time. He had about as much chance winning with both eyes open as he did with both eyes closed. Along with his Triple Crown Whirlaway was a two-time Horse-of-the-Year. How's that, college boy? I bet they never taught you anything like that at school."

"No sir, we were up to our necks in the Pythagorean Principle."

"Really, and here I thought you didn't know your Isosceles Triangle from a hole in the ground."

"Leonard, I didn't know you used that kind of language."

It wasn't often I was able to take one of Leonard's quips and improve upon it, but from the volume of his belly

161

laugh I'd have to say I did. "You know, Jimmy lived and worked in his father's shadow practically all his life. The funny thing was that it was Jimmy who solved the mystery of how to get Whirlaway to run, and he was also the person who developed Citation, but at the time his father was still being listed as the trainer-of-record on all of Calumet's horses. Mr. Ben is credited with a record six Kentucky Derby winners. Jimmy has officially two to his credit, but Lord knows he's had a big hand in his Daddy's six. They were a great team, maybe the best."

At that moment we pulled back into the restaurant parking lot, right next to my car. "Leonard, I'd like to hear the rest of the story; but I know you need to get home."

He copied the Clemens' shrug and leapt out of the car. He tapped the top of the truck a couple times and made his way to the store's front porch. "Well, are you comin' or not?" He reached under the bench and pulled out a bucket. As I got closer, even with all the lights off; I could see it was filled with ice and a couple bottles.

"A beer would hit the spot." I said.

"Root beer does more than hit the spot, it fills it up." Leonard popped open a bottle and handed it to me. "I told 'em to put a couple out here for us, I had a feeling we'd be ready for one right about now."

I took a swig and again, as always, Leonard was right. That old fashioned root beer was perfect. Leonard had taken me on a fanciful tour over hundreds of years of racing trivia and in the process he had appealed to every sense. I could see the Dream Race, I could hear it, I felt it, and around the stalls I even smelt it. This cold root beer was just what the track vet would have ordered. It was sugar-filled nostalgia. Leonard popped another bottle cap and joined me on the road full of memories and finish lines.

"Devil red and blue," Leonard said with his eyes glued to his bottle.

"Calumet's silks." I was beginning to be able to follow the path of his thoughts. In a short time, the two of us had gone from nothing in common; to the point where I realized we were a whole lot more alike than we were different. He was a teacher and I was his student. He was a man and I was his friend. You can go a lifetime and never find either a teacher or a friend. So, when you can find both in the same person, you

have to take a moment to appreciate how truly lucky you've been.

"Luck's got nothing to with it," Leonard said.

"What's that?"

"Luck, you were just thinking about luck."

"What . . . how, I mean . . . what makes you say that?" Was he really reading my mind?

"Horse racing always involves luck, but luck seemed to be good friends with Calumet. Some might say luck's favorite colors were devil red and blue."

Luck and friends; Leonard used the terms in a different context and even tied it back into our conversation about Calumet. I turned up my bottle and polished it in a blink of an eye.

"The way you knocked off that bottle reminds me of a story about two bulls up on a hill looking down at a herd of cows . . ."

"An old bull and a young bull." We both smiled.

"I guess you've heard it." Leonard said.

"You tell me."

"Yeah, Twain, I guess you have."

"Why don't I tell you about Bull Lea instead; after all he is the cornerstone to Calumet's rise to prominence." Leonard looked at his root beer. He had barely touched it, then he looked at my empty bottle. "Next time, the young bull won't be in such a hurry." He sat down on the bench and motioned for me to join him.

"It's a crime this horse ain't in the Horse Racing Hall-of-Fame. I mean, he's been responsible for more horses, trainers, and owners going in there than just about any other horse. His race record was better than some in the hall, but he was such a great sire that his race record has been almost forgotten over time."

"Criminal," I snapped. Leonard had come to expect my snide remarks. It was late and when you're tired, you resort back to what comes natural. "Someone needs to be locked up."

"Yeah, and that someone is you." Leonard reached back in the bucket and handed me another root beer. "No one knows a young bull better than an old bull." On that note we clanked our bottles together.

163

"So, I guess little Jimmy was the young bull."

"Yeah, probably a lot like you." The only thing keeping Leonard from smiling was the bottle he popped into his mouth.

"And Ben Jones . . . ?"

"Well, we've both lived a lot of years and almost every one of them spent around horses."

"That sounds like a bunch of old bull if you ask me."

The words were no sooner out of my mouth than Leonard was spitting out a mouthful of root beer. Leonard wiped his mouth and jokingly wiped his hand on my shoulder and then the other.

"I knight thee, Sir Twain." It wasn't a sword, but I felt like royalty anyhow. I looked at my shirt as if I had found a root beer stain. "Don't worry, baking powder will take that out. I'd recommend the Calumet brand."

"Calumet baking powder?"

"Yeah, Calumet; sound familiar? That's where the money for the farm came from. Mr. Warren Wright converted his father's Standardbred farm into a thoroughbred farm in '32, but it was the family's baking powder company that made it all possible."

"Man, that's a lot of baking powder. Oh, now I get it; the sweetest cake ever baked by Calumet."

"Yeah, but all the money in the world and the best of intentions on Mr. Wright's part to breed and race the best horses was washing a lot of baking powder down the drain before he brought on the Joneses. After that the horse world spent the next twenty-something years playing an expensive game of keeping-up-with-the-Joneses."

Another sip was punctuation.

"Let me give you some facts. During the fifty years Calumet was owned by Mr. Wright or his widow, they won over twenty-four hundred races and over five hundred of 'em were stakes races. That's ten stakes races per year for fifty years or nearly fifty wins per year for fifty years. Think about it; that's like winning one race per week, every week for fifty years. Let's make one thing for sure, that's a lot of luck and whole lot of something else."

"Good horses?"

"Great horses and great people; and that combination turned a lot of baking powder into a lot of bread. During one fifteen year period, Calumet was on top of the money list twelve times and never out of the top three. They have eight horses in the Horse Racing Hall-of-Fame, most farms are fortunate, if they can hang that title on even one stall door. We talked about Tim Tam injuring his leg in the Belmont or he would have been their third Triple Crown winner. Remember Calumet's Alydar was the horse battling Affirmed every step of the way in '78 to the last Triple Crown. Coaltown was supposed to be the best horse in the barn at the start of '48, the only horse better than Coaltown in the whole country was his stall-mate, Citation. The '47 Horse-of-the-Year, Armed, kept going to the races and kept bringing back wins making him one of the top Iron Horses of all-time. Matter of fact, Calumet owned the Horse-of-the-Year in '41, '42, '44, '47, and '48. Mind you, 99.9% of farms out there will spend their entire racing careers and never have one Horse-of-the-Year or Hall-of-Fame Horse. Davona Dale, Real Delight, and Wistful all won the fillies' version of the Triple Crown. Calumet set the bar at unbelievable heights in an era when horse racing was under the public microscope. Racing was the national pastime before baseball.

"Speaking of that, I'll give you another comparison; take the New York Yankees and pick their best players over the last century. You'd have a lot of Hall-of-Famers, some of the biggest names in the sport. That may be your best comparison: baseball's Yankees with Ruth, Gerhig, DiMaggio, Yogi Berra, Mantle, Maris, Reggie Jackson, Thurmon Munson, and Mattingly versus the line up of Whirlaway, Bull Lea, Armed, Twilight Tear, Citation, Coaltown, Tim Tam, Iron Liege, Forward Pass, Pensive, Ponder, Two Lea, Real Delight, Bewitched, Davona Dale, and Alydar."

"I guess you'd have Casey Stengel managing against the Joneses."

"Casey Stengel?" Leonard sounded mildly surprised.

"Well, I am a sports writer; I have to know something about the great dynasties, don't I?"

"You really did buy the Baseball Encyclopedia, didn't you?" Leonard held out his bottle and we clanked them together again. "Twenty-five or twenty-six world championships in eighty years for the Yankees . . .and they dominate the Baseball Hall-of-Fame."

"And you still believe Calumet was the dynasty of all dynasties." I said.

Leonard nodded, "Indeed I do. Indeed I do." then kicked back another swig. "Maybe it's because I'm a horseman. Maybe it's because Arcaro never faced a hundred mile an hour fastball, but the Babe never rode Citation either. You know, Calumet won two Triple Crowns and so have the Yankees with Lou Gerhig and Mickey Mantle. Calumet's devil red silks and the Yankees' pin stripes represent the same long term tradition, and dedication to success and winning. If Calumet was stuck smack dab in the middle of New York City, then there'd be absolutely no difference."

"Ah, the advantage of being a media capital. Leonard, I'm curious, what changed at Calumet?"

"When Mrs. Markey died in '82 the farm went through a real tough time financially. The rumors ran faster than their horses and wilder than Whirlaway without blinkers. The future of the farm dangled by a thread after some difficult years. A white knight rode to the rescue in the '90s in the form of a count, Count Kwaitkowski from Poland and a real horseman in the great East European tradition."

"Kowakowa . . .whatski?"

"Count Kwaitowski, he loved the horses and restored Calumet to a level of respect. The Calumet horses again began to challenge at the classics under the world's spotlight. When the Count bought the farm the Devil red and blue silks were not part of the deal."

"Why not?"

"The Calumet Trust for the estate wanted an additional fee for the use of their silks and the Count had enough of the board-room three-card-monty."

"Really? It makes you wonder why they call it a 'trust'," I said.

"There's no doubt those silks were worth something, but Mr. Kwaitowski already had to pay extra to use the Calumet name and wasn't going to do the same to use the silks."

"Nothing quite like putting it to the white knight."

"The Count passed away, signaling more changes at Calumet. No one knows what the future holds for one of the greatest dynasties racing has ever seen; but it's definitely time to change the page on the calendar of racing history." Leonard finished his thought with another sip of pop.

"I got it; it's the end of the day. So, this Calumet race is the last of the Dream Races and it's at sunset, right? Yeah, I can see . . . well, kind of, where is this race taking place?"

"Right next door to Calumet," was Leonard's answer.

"On their own training track?"

"Might as well be, but no. Actually, this one is at Keeneland. Calumet and Keeneland back up to each other. As much as Lexington is the center of horse racing in this country, Keeneland is the epicenter and Calumet was right at the center of it all. Now, picture this: every jockey has the devil red and blue silks with more than a dozen horses. Four Horses-of-the-Year, two of them Triple Crown winners, eight Hall-of-Fame horses, two Hall-of-Fame trainers, and all of them set against the backdrop of Keeneland at sunset."

"It sounds beautiful."

"Oh, it gets just a little bit better. You see, Keeneland is the only track that faces west. All tracks are set so the crowd can sit in the shade and not have to stare into the sun. One of the prettiest sights in racing is the way the sun reflects off the club house glass windows like a mirror. Only at Keeneland can the end of the day be prolonged in reflection." Leonard swirled his almost empty bottle.

"So, the sunset is symbolic as much as it is aesthetic."

"Pretty too." Leonard said with a wink and then turned the bottle straight up to get the last drop. "Speaking of the end of the day, I think I'm as done as this bottle and with that, so is the Dream Race." Leonard stood and started towards his truck. I was still picturing the sunset at Keeneland when I realized he was leaving.

"Hey, Leonard, you never told me who won the Dream Race. Who's the greatest of all-time?"

"Twain, you're the one writing the article; why don't you tell me?" That was the last thing Leonard said before he jumped in his truck; not good-bye or see you later. I shrugged my shoulders as his red tail-lights faded in the distance. I knew he was right . . . again.

The Dream Race

Epilogue

A couple of days after spending the whole day with Leonard hearing about the Dream Race I returned to find Leonard. I went to Memaw's at 5:00 in the morning. Unlike the first time I was here, I was wide awake and excited. I couldn't wait to find Leonard. My first article had been published and I wanted Leonard to be the first person I shared it with. I looked around the restaurant. I saw the cherub-faced waitress. She didn't recognize me at first, maybe it was because my zipper was up this time. Maybe it was because my hair was combed, my faced freshly shaved, and I was actually awake. I spotted Leonard in his usual booth. The expression on his face when he first saw me was one of surprise.

"Good morning, Leonard."

"I see your manners have improved and you're getting better at dressing yourself, too."

Without another word I dropped the newspaper on the table in front of him. He looked at me and smiled. "It's good isn't it, Twain?"

"Read it."

"Oh, I'm going to, but I don't have to read it to know it's good. It's written all over your face." Leonard reached his hand across the table to shake mine. I don't know why, but I started getting tears in my eyes. Leonard pulled a couple napkins out of the dispenser and set one in front of me, while holding onto the other for himself. "Sit down, boy. I can't read it with you standing over me." He picked up the paper and flipped to my article and began to read:

The Dream Race –

The Search for the Greatest Horse of All-Time - -

By Allen Clemens

This is my first article for the paper and with any luck it won't be my last. I must confess; Mr. Williams, my boss, and to many of you, your children's Sunday School teacher, is a very sneaky man. Don't worry, before you go pulling your kids out of his class; I mean that with the deepest respect. The subject of this article was presented to me as just an assignment. I later learned that it was a test of my skills. That's a pretty devious way of testing the new kid, but what I didn't realize until later, it was a test and a lesson all in one. I learned a lot about horses in the process, but that's not the lesson I'm referring to. No, this was a lesson about people; better yet, it was a lesson about judging people. No doubt, this was a test I was destined to fail, if it hadn't been for one very special person. He took the time to teach me about horses, but even more about people and most importantly – a lot about myself.

He is a walking encyclopedia about the history of thoroughbred racing, but most of all he is a wise man, not just in intelligence. He has plenty of that, but he is a wise man in terms of his connection with who he is and who each and everyone of us are when all the trimmings are removed. To use the terms sage or oracle may seem a bit far fetched, but once you've had a chance to get know him and his story the flattery is clearly based in reality. Leonard Tharpe prefers for me not use his name . . . oops, sorry about that, my friend. This story is his story. I am only the messenger of his story; and in the process an ambassador to history. When I am finished, I hope as I am sure Leonard does, it becomes your story to do with as you will; my advice would be to share it.

The first thing you have to understand about racing is that there is no winner until the race is run; everything leading up to that moment is purely speculation. Horses settle all the debate in one simple way; on the track. Stop watches, racing forms, magazines, gossip, and (this is the part where I may lose my job) even newspapers are worthless when the bell sounds. "They're off!" is probably Latin for "Throw it all away". Hours boasting of racing knowledge are quickly replaced in a few quick minutes with enlightened truth. In the starting gate, they're all potential champions; at the wire there is only one who can continue bragging. Of course that time in the spotlight only lasts until the next time the bell sounds and someone else stands in the winner's circle getting their picture taken.

Greatness isn't a fleeting moment. Greatness stands the test of time and isn't snatched away by a nose in a photo finish a week later. Greatness isn't a crown passed from one horse to another like hand-me-down cloths. It is a legacy shared by each generation. There are stories of heroes, phenomenal accomplishments, and unbridled spirit from our royal courtiers each staking their claim. Yet, in the quest to honor the single 'Greatest', we are expected to rule out all challengers to the throne and anoint one king. In the back of my mind I hear a chorus of a joyous crowd yelling at the top of their lungs, "The king is dead, long live the king"; I have to wonder how often a new king is celebrated in this raucous manner.

The Dream Race takes place in heaven. Do you know what heaven is? Heaven is Hialeah in the winter, Churchill Downs in May, Belmont in June, Saratoga in the summer, and Santa Anita in the fall. Heaven is the opening day at a track that doesn't exist any more where the pink flamingos bathed in the open oblivious to the horses flying past them; the same way the horses ignore them when they circle the track. Heaven is a blanket of roses, Black-Eyed-Susans draped over a horse's back, or 350 quilted white carnations. Heaven is ivy covered grandstands glimmering in the wind. Heaven is timeless architecture and gardens filled with sculptures honoring the past. It's tradition. It's where the past and the present embrace like old friends who have spent far too much time apart. It is a future of hope and dreams of what could be. Heaven is a place where being the greatest is not nearly as important as we mortals make it out to be.

To name one horse and say, this is the 'greatest of all-time' seems to make perfect sense to us earth-bound souls. That's what humans do; we riddle ourselves with questions that have thousands of possibilities and expect to be content with one simple answer. The question of who is the greatest horse is one for people to debate, but maybe better left unanswered. But, if an answer must be determined, then let the horses decide the answer and let them settle it their way, on a track in a place called heaven.

When he finished, the first thing Leonard did was dry his eyes with the napkin. Seeing his response made me do the same. "Twain, it's perfect. It's heaven."

"Thank you, I couldn't have . . . ."

"Would you sign this copy for me?" Leonard asked.

"This one's getting all messed up, I have a new one in the car."

"No, this is the one I want. This is the one you brought to me and this is the one I want to put in my room with all my others." Leonard's remark was as high a compliment as I could have asked for. Without another word I pulled a pen from my pocket, signed my name, and scribbled these words:

LEONARD, SEE YOU AT THE DREAM RACE – ALLEN

The Dream Race

Leonard and I stayed in touch as often as possible. Breakfast at Memaw's became a regular meeting place for us. I never thought I would say this, but 5:00 in the morning is a great time of day. Hearing Leonard's stories made getting up before sunrise a treat. He continued to tell me stories about horses, lots of horses; but more than that, he continued to teach me little things about life every time we got together.

I was fortunate to have known Leonard for a few years before he passed away, Thelma followed him within a month or so. I still think of them both often. The way they lived their lives was example of what real happiness truly is. Even after they were gone they continued to walk the talk. In their wills they left all of their money to charity. Some were dedicated to helping children get an education, others to aid in caring for horses retired from racing, and another for equine research.

The two of them had accumulated a pretty nifty sum over their years. Leonard made one last codicil to his will. He passed all of the items in his private museum to me. It was both an honor and one last lesson from a teacher to his student.

When I dissembled Leonard's shrine of nostalgia, one of the items I came across was a crumpled newspaper column. It was my first article for the newspaper. It was the story of the Dream Race and more specifically, it was the one I had inscribed to him. I quietly folded the article and placed inside my wallet next to an old tattered sheet of blue lined paper with names of several horses that I had since put to memory. It had stayed in my wallet since the day I met Leonard.

"Yes, my friend, I will see you at the Dream Race. I'll know where to find you."

Dream Race: The Search for the Greatest Thoroughbred Race Horse of All-Time

Let the search begin with eleven Triple Crown winners, a dozen near misses, and a bunch of crowd favorites. Thirty-five (35) of the horses in **Dream Race** can be found in the 'Dream Race Puzzle'. See how many you can find. For the answers you can go to the author's web site: www.robertclark.us

Sir Barton	1919	Pleasant Colony
Gallant Fox	1930	Ribot
Omaha	1935	Riva Ridge
War Admiral	1937	Roamer
Whirlaway	1941	Cigar
Count Fleet	1943	Dr. Fager
Assault	1946	Funny(*cide*)
Citation	1948	Genuine Risk
Secretariat	1973	(*go for*) Wand
Seattle Slew	1977	Godolphin
Affirmed	1978	Man O' War
Armed		Native Dancer
Bold (*ruler*)		Round (*table*)
Buck(*passer*)		Ruffian
Bull (*lea*)		Seabiscuit
Silver Charm		Swaps
Smarty (*jones*)		Winning Colors
Swale		

```
Y N O L O C T N A S A E L P E N
R O A M E R O U N D E M A D G E
T R J T R A W O N A M C I Y G L
S E A B I S C U I T E O A N O A
E A R G O V A R A G R U H N D W
W S K E I N E O R O E N A U O S
I K N O X C W D L O B T M F L M
N S O E G A L L A N T F O X P A
N I I O R F N O A N E L R A H R
I R T A I R A T E R C E S R I T
N E A A G R I B O T D E S M N Y
G N T S A V F V N T E T R E O A
C I I S E A F R A R M O E D T W
O U C A S B U C K R R E M A R A
L N N U W A R A D M I R A L A L
O E P L S P A W S P F D O M B R
R G L T E O R I D R F A G E R I
S U S I L V E R C H A R M E I H
B D N A W E L S E L T T A E S W
```

The Dream Race

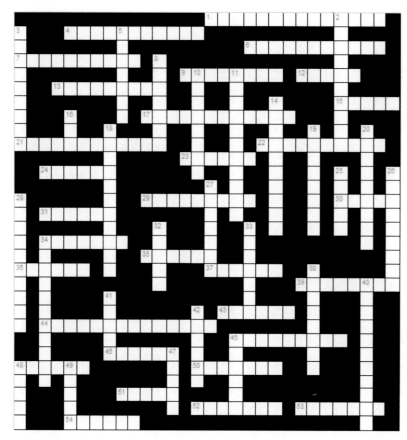

Dream Race Crossword Puzzle©

Across

1) Undefeated filly (pg.28)
4) 30 length win in Belmont (pg.51)
6) Wins first two classics '99 (pg.96)
7) Iron horse with 43 wins (pg.40)
8) Belair Stud's fastest (pg.37)
12) 1908 undefeated colt (pg.74)
13) Star of the book <u>King Of Wind</u> (pg.62)
15) Tied Citation's 16 consecutive win streak (pg.125)
17) First filly Horse-of-the-Year (pg.27)
21) Gray Ghost (pg.33)
22) 1930 Triple Crown winner (pg.143)
23) First filly to win Kentucky Derby (pg.23)

29) Born the same day as Round Table (pg.39)
30) Filly 2002 Horse-of-the-Year (pg.27)
31) Had 131 starts (pg.118)
34) Europe's Horse-of-the-Century (pg.110)
35) East coast rival of Swaps (pg.35)
36) 4-time handicap Horse-of-the-Year (pg.127)
37) Tesio's great producing undefeated stallion (pg.108)
39) UK's first Triple Crown winner in 40 years in 1970. (pg.109)
43) Foundation stallion from Syria (pg.60)
44) Safety pin stopped his Triple Crown bid. (pg. 92)
45) The closest to winning the Triple Crown after Affirmed. (pg.97)
46) Second in all three Triple Crown races (pg.49)
48) '89 near miss, _____ Silence (pg.91)
50) The Clubfooted Comet (pg.148)
51) 5-time Horse-of-the-Year (pg.34)
52) Australian legend (pg.106)
53) Named after the doctor who saved his trainers life (pg.36)
54) Colin's grandsire (pg.74)

Down

2) Beat War Admiral in match race (pg.85) movie star
3) First Triple Crown winner (pg. 143)
8) Horse-of-the-Year Awards are named after him. (pg.76)
10) 1978 Triple Crown winner (pg. 88)
11) Nicknamed Baby Huey (pg.51)
14) 4th Triple Crown winner (pg.85)
16) Won $300,000 in 1920's (pg.144)
18) Secretariat's best filly (pg.19)
19) _____ Prince (pg.38)
20) Won over $4 million (pg.126)
25) Passed away 3 days after winning Belmont Stakes (pg. 99)
26) Nicknamed Mr. Longtail (pg.147)
27) Filly in the tragic match race with Foolish Pleasure (pg.24)
28) Owned by the founder of Hertz Rental Cars (pg.147)
32) West coast rival of Nashua (pg.35)
33) Kidnapped by the IRA? (pg.107)
34) "the charm of Marilyn Monroe" (pg.26)
38) First horse to win $million – 1948 Triple Crown winner (pg.35)
41) Only son of a Triple Crown winner to win the Triple Crown (pg.145)
42) Finished the Belmont with a injured leg, costing him a Triple Crown (pg.42)
45) Result of a chance mating of teaser with a blind mare (pg.121)
47) Italian stallion in Kentucky (pg.104)
48) Azeri broke her filly money record (pg.28)
49) Beat the '46 Triple Crown winner in a match race (pg.119)

Answers:
    in the book or at www.robertclark.us

HORSE & DRAGON

PUBLISHING

Dream Race

Order Form

E-mail orders – orders@horsedragon.com

Toll-free telephone orders – 877-374-6815

Fax orders: 321-821-2226

Postal orders:

Horse & Dragon Publishing

PO Box 372388

Satellite Beach, FL 32937

Company: _____

Name: _____

Address: _____

_____

City: _____

State: _____ Zip: _____

Telephone: ( ) _____

E-mail: _____

☐ Check – payable to **Horse & Dragon Publishing**

☐ Credit card: (Circle one) **VISA, MasterCard, Amex, Discover**

Card number _____

Name on card _____

Expiration date _____ Security Code _____

Order Now

Horse & Dragon Publishing offers you the opportunity to buy additional copies of the ***Dream Race*** book(s) $39.95 (+shipping) or prints of the ***Dream Race*** art.
The complete Set of 12 prints (9"x 12") for $125.00 (+shipping), or individually for $20.00 per print (9"x12" + shipping).
-See Reverse Side-

The Dream Race

Order Form

Qty	Item	Price	Sub Total
_____	*Dream Race* book(s)	$39.95	_____
_____	Complete set of 12 prints	$125.00	_____
_____	Ladies First (9"x12")	$20.00	_____
_____	Between Crowns (9"x12")	$20.00	_____
_____	Superfreaks (9"x12")	$20.00	_____
_____	The Three Kings (9"x12")	$20.00	_____
_____	Eclipse First (9"x12")	$20.00	_____
_____	Men of War (9"x12")	$20.00	_____
_____	After Affirmed (9"x12")	$20.00	_____
_____	Global Gauntlet (9"x12")	$20.00	_____
_____	Iron Horses (9"x12")	$20.00	_____
_____	Trinity (9"x12")	$20.00	_____
_____	The Fourth Crown (9"x12")	$20.00	_____
_____	All Good Things (9"x12")	$20.00	_____
		Sub Total	_____

Florida residents add 6%   _____

Shipping add: $6.95 for artwork _____
$6.95 for first book _____
$5.00 for each add'l book _____

Order total $ _____

Ladies First   Between Crowns   Superfreaks

Three Kings   Eclipse First   Men O' War

After Affirmed   Global Gauntlet   Iron Horses

Trinity   Fourth Crown   All Good Things

To view or purchase **original artwork** and/or **limited edition prints**

go to **www.robertclark.us**